CW00794694

# SAMOAN HERBAL MEDICINE

## 'O Lā'au ma Vai Fofō o Samoa

by

### Dr. W. Arthur Whistler
### Botany Department, University of Hawai'i

**Published for O le Siosiomaga Society Inc.
of Western Samoa**

**1996**

Published by Isle Botanica
500 University Ave. # 1601
Honolulu, Hawaii 96826 U.S.A.

Library of Congress No. 95-082217
ISBN: 0-9645426-2-5
Copyright 1996 by W. Arthur Whistler
All rights reserved

Printed by Thomson-Shore, Inc., Dexter, Michigan

This book is lovingly dedicated to Patricia Whistler Kerr, for her continued interest in my South Seas trips, and for starting me down the long slippery slope to Botany so many years ago.

All photos were taken by the author.

COVER: The tools of the trade of a Savai'i healer: cutting board, rock pestles, giant clam shell, kitchen knife, glass, spoon, tin can, matches, cloth, coconut shell, and a bottle of coconut oil.

# PREFACE

The use of medicinal plants dates back to prehistoric times when ancient man found that ingestion or application of certain herbs and barks were effective in treating some of the ailments that plagued him. Herbal medicine is part of virtually all cultures, and Samoa is no exception. However, most observers of Samoan society during the early stages of European contact in the mid-19th century noted only insignificant use of herbal medicines, particularly those taken internally. Whether or not this is accurate may never be known conclusively, but today in Samoa a large segment of the population takes or is given Samoan herbal medicine sometime during their lifetime, especially during infancy and childhood. Thus, despite 165 years of contact with Western culture and its medical traditions, Samoan herbal medicine is strong today, and does not appear to be in danger of dying out in the near future. What may be disappearing, however, are the remedies that rely on plants that are becoming increasing scarce, a problem that needs to be addressed by conservation programs.

The study of herbal medicine involves the fusion of several sciences—medicine, pharmacology, sociology, and botany. My original interest in herbal medicine began with my employment at the National Tropical Botanical Garden of Hawai'i as an "ethnobotanist," one who studies how various cultures, particularly those of developing countries, utilize the plant life in their environment. Ethnobotanical information has often been collected by scientists lacking training in botany, which has sometimes resulted in incorrect identification of the plants utilized. My background in plant taxonomy (the classification of plants) and studies of the Polynesian flora (1971 to the present) have hopefully allowed me to overcome some of the previous deficiencies in the study of herbal medicine in the islands. However, a medical or pharmacological degree and a sound basis in sociology would have also been extremely useful in the study of Samoan herbal medicine.

Being a scientist, I am by nature skeptical of unsubstantiated claims of "miracle cures" that are so often attributed to herbal medicines, especially by those who have a commercial interest in promoting their philosophy and/or products. Although medicinal plants such as rauvolfia, digitalis, and Madagascar periwinkle, and even the recently popular aloe, are undoubtedly of tremendous value, each claim of healing properties attributed to a plant must be studied scientifically to rule out a "placebo effect," "old wives' tales," and outright fraud to accurately access the value of the remedies.

Eighty-four plants commonly used by native healers in Samoa are listed in Chapter III. The fact that I have tried few of these can be attributed to several reasons: (1) I am basically skeptical, as noted above; (2) I fortunately am healthy by nature and have few ailments to test them on; and (3) it is not for me, a botanist, to do a doctor's or pharmaceutical researcher's job. Consequently, I would personally recommend very few of the 84 plants listed in Chapter III. In fact, the healers themselves do not believe the herbal medicines work for anyone who makes unauthorized use of the owner's remedy! Also, since no dosages are noted in the medicinal uses listed, it could be dangerous to take any of the internal remedies without proper supervision. Even *with* supervision, it can be dangerous. In a case from Hawai'i in 1982, a Samoan healer prepared a potion from a plant (known by botanists to be poisonous) and gave half to his patient and half to himself; the patient soon died of respiratory failure and the healer ended up in the hospital.

The discussion in the following chapters is presented with the hope that it will convey a description of the Samoan system of herbal medicine—what it was originally like, how and why it evolved, and how it functions today. The enumeration of the plants and their uses is simply for the benefit of interested persons who wish to learn which plants are used (effectively or ineffectively) for ailments in Samoa.

However, the presentation in this book has unavoidable limitations because it is impossible for an outsider, even one who speaks the language (to a degree) and has lived in the culture for eight years (as the author has) to fully understand Samoan medicine. This shortcoming, hopefully, is counter-balanced by the scientific context in which the information is presented, backed by information in publications of previous authors dating back 165 years.

The orthography used in the following text is based on the Samoan dictionary (Milner 1966), which includes glottal stops (often written as an apostrophe or inverted apostrophe) between vowels that are pronounced separately, and a line (a "macron") over vowels that are stressed. Although these are usually omitted in everyday writing by Samoans, they are included here for clarity. The word "Samoa" is actually written in Samoan as Sāmoa, but this spelling is followed only in Samoan words.

Art Whistler
Honolulu, Hawaii
December 1995

# ACKNOWLEDGMENTS

I would like to thank Dion Ale, Totoa Lualua, and Eleni Wheeler for their superb efforts as my translators and guides in Western Samoa, American Samoa, and New Zealand, respectively, during my field work on three research trips in 1994. I would also like to thank Dr. Cluny and Sisi Macpherson, Epi Enari, Fata Simanu-Klutz, Sharon Crichton, Papali 'i Afele, and Dr. Anne Shovic for their proofreading of the manuscript, Clyde Imada for his editing, the Rev. Malo Tanielu of Letui for his help in contacting healers, and Koroseta To'o and the staff of the O le Siosiomaga Society of Western Samoa for their excellent technical support throughout the project.

I am also greatly indebted to Diane Goodwillie and the Canadian Fund for so generously funding this project through the O le Siosiomaga Society. But most of all, I am indebted to the twenty-seven *taulāsea* who so graciously shared their healing knowledge with me during the interviews. They are as follows: Lusia Tupuola of Mangere (New Zealand), Lauamanu Fonoti and Kalala of Auckland (New Zealand), Tauilemete Lilo and Iva Mamoa of Aopo, Solosolo Tala Peleuila and Nu'utai Afitu of Letui, Fa'asi'u Tiotala Tavita and Sailau Iosefa of Salelologa, Lefe'e Mete of Fa'ala, Pusi Neumi Lama of Vaitele, Sina Tuiavi'i of Uafato, Auta'ele Falefa of Sale'imoa, Li'a Paleafe and Faleupolu Tuiasau of Lauli'i (Tutuila), Mele Lualua of Vaitogi (Tutuila), Kilisi Stowers of Pava'ia'i (Tutuila), 'Ele'ele Matavao of Tafuna (Tutuila), Fa'afete Galo and Olive Talaia of Moata'a, Sina Ataga and Ema Lopeti of Magiagi, Gagau Tapumanaia of Leone, Tauvasa Afiafi of Tanugamanono, Amela Tugaga of Tafituala, and Fa'aasu Fuamatu and Taufaunia Tovia of Fagali'i.


# ABOUT THE AUTHOR

Art Whistler was born near Death Valley, California, to which he attributes his early love of plants and vegetation. After receiving a B.A. and an M.A. at the University of California, he served three years with the U.S. Peace Corps in Western Samoa where he taught high school biology. Resuming his schooling, he received a Ph.D. in Botany at the University of Hawai'i in 1979. Since then he has made numerous research trips to Samoa, Tonga, the Cook Islands, Tahiti, and elsewhere in the Pacific, working on the ethnobotany, medicinal plants, and flora of the islands. He has published several books on the botany of the Pacific Islands, including *Polynesian Herbal Medicine* (1992a) and *Tongan Herbal Medicine* (1992b), has written numerous scientific articles on medicinal plants, ethnobotany, and floristics of Polynesia, and is an adjunct Associate Professor with the Botany Department of the University of Hawai'i.

# TABLE OF CONTENTS

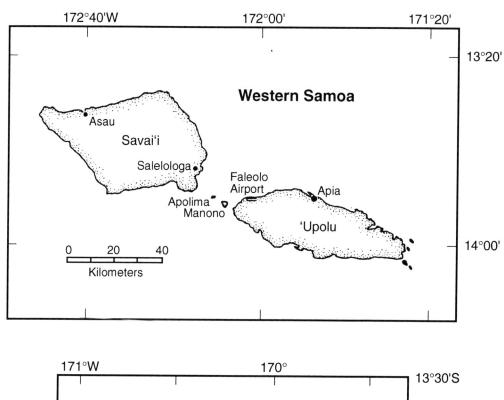

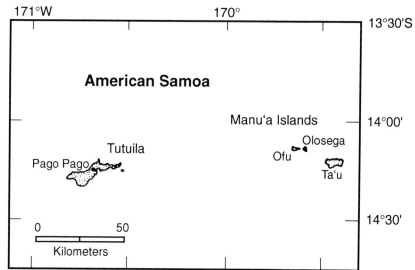

Fig. 1. Maps of Western and American Samoa

# INTRODUCTION

## THE ISLANDS

Samoa is a volcanic archipelago situated in the South Pacific Ocean at a latitude of 13—15° South and a longitude of 168—173° West, and runs in a west-northwest direction east of Fiji, north of Tonga, south of Tokelau, and west of Niue and the Cook Islands (Fig. 1). Its nine inhabited islands and several uninhabited islets, plus two distant coral islands, have a total area of ca. 3100 km².

The archipelago is divided politically into Western Samoa, which is an independent country, and American Samoa, which is an unincorporated territory of the United States; the two are separated by a strait 64 km wide. Western Samoa is by far the larger of the two, and makes up about 93% of the land area of the archipelago. It comprises the main islands of Savai'i (1820 km²) and 'Upolu (1110 km²), which are separated by a strait 21 km wide. Between the two are the small islands Apolima and Manono.

American Samoa consists of five main volcanic islands and two atolls. The largest of the islands is Tutuila (124 km²), and lying off its southeastern end is the small volcanic cone island of 'Aunu'u. Approximately 100 km to the east lies the group of islands known as Manu'a, which comprises Ta'ū (39 km²), 'Ofu (5 km²), and 'Olosega (4 km²). One hundred and forty km to the east of Ta'ū lies uninhabited Rose Atoll, and 320 km north lies Swains Island, which is home to a small population.

Since Samoa is situated between the tropic of Capricorn and the Equator, its climate is tropical. Typical temperatures (at sea level) are between 24—29°C (75—84°F) throughout the year. The difference between the average temperature of winter (June to September) and summer (December to March) is only about 2°C (4°F), and the average annual temperature is about 26°C (79°F). The relative humidity is constantly high, averaging about 80%. Rainfall is heavy throughout the archipelago, with a minimum of 200 cm on the main islands.

## CULTURE AND HISTORY

Culturally, Samoa is part of western Polynesia, which comprises the two main archipelagoes of Tonga and Samoa, and the smaller islands of Niue, Tuvalu (formerly called the Ellice Islands), Wallis Island, the Horne Islands (Futuna and Alofi), and several other islands scattered in Micronesia and Melanesia that are called "Polynesian outliers." Fiji, which is geographically part of Melanesia, is culturally part of western Polynesia instead. Western Polynesia is distinguished from eastern Polynesia (including Tahiti, Hawai'i, and New Zealand) by cultural and linguistic differences, and the two areas were virtually isolated from each other for over 16 centuries until the arrival of the Europeans, which began in earnest in 1769.

The earliest traces of habitation in Samoa date to about 1000 B.C., when ancient Polynesians (collectively and anthropologically referred to as the "Lapita culture") colonized the archipelago from nearby islands, probably from Tonga, which was perhaps settled a little earlier than Samoa. The two archipelagoes developed their own cultures

1

and languages, but for several centuries (perhaps in the 1500s and/or 1600s) Samoa was conquered and ruled by Tongans before they were driven out. There was also some contact with Fiji during this long period of time, but less than with Tonga.

The first contact with Europeans was probably in 1722, when Jacob Roggeveen passed through Samoan waters, but did not land. Louis de Bougainville also passed through Samoan waters without landing (1768), but gave the archipelago its first European name, the "Navigator Islands." The first recorded landing was by la Pérouse in 1787, when his expedition anchored at A'asu on the northwestern coast of Tutuila. This landing was abruptly terminated by a battle between the French and the Samoans, which caused other Westerners to generally steer clear of the archipelago for another 40 years.

Then in 1830 Rev. John Williams of the London Missionary Society (L.M.S.) visited Samoa, leading to the establishment of Christianity in the islands and the beginning of major changes in Samoan society. For the next seven decades Samoa became a pawn in a power struggle between European and American powers, culminating in the permanent division of the archipelago into American Samoa and Western Samoa. The latter was originally a German colony, but control was given to New Zealand by the League of Nations after World War I. It was not until 1962 that Western Samoa became an independent country. The government is a democracy with a Prime Minister, Head of State, and parliament, and universal suffrage was recently implemented, although candidates must be *matai* (chiefs) in order to run for office (except for two seats reserved for candidates of European descent). American Samoa remains an unincorporated territory of the United States, but elects its own legislature and governor.

Although the two parts of the archipelago are separated politically, they are inhabited by a single people who speak the same language (with only minor vocabulary and accent differences). The current population of Western Samoa is estimated to be over 168,000, and that of American Samoa over 46,000 (and very rapidly increasing). Samoan herbal medicine is practiced in both Samoas in almost identical ways, and, in fact, many of the healers in American Samoa are originally from Western Samoa. Thus, the discussion in the rest of this book applies equally well to both Western and American Samoa.

## THE FLORA OF SAMOA

The "flora" of Samoa (i.e., the sum of all the plants present in the islands) includes flowering vascular plants (monocots and dicots), non-flowering vascular plants (including ferns), and all other plants (including algae, lichens, etc.). However, for the study of herbal medicine, the most important species are the vascular plants, and these are the ones that will be emphasized in this book. Only a single lower plant, a lichen (*Ramalina* sp.?), has been recorded as being medicinal in Samoa, and only one fern (**lau 'autā**, *Phymatosorus scolopendria*) is commonly used.

Plant species can be classified by their distribution: they are either *native*, i.e., they are naturally occurring in the area (arrived by natural means) or they are *introduced* (arrived by direct or indirect human transport). The native flora of Samoa consists of about 230 species of ferns and "fern allies," and 540 species of flowering plants.

Introduced species are further divided into intentional and unintentional introductions. Another name for an introduced plant is "alien species," a term that has recently become popular. *Intentional* introductions are species that were purposefully brought into an area; these are usually crop plants, such as breadfruit, taro, and yams, or ornamentals, such as the red hibiscus and Tahitian gardenia. *Unintentional* introductions are species that were accidentally introduced into an area, and are mostly "weeds" that are naturalized in disturbed habitats. Introduced species are sometimes classified by time of introduction; those brought in before the European Era (beginning in ca. 1830 in Samoa) are called "Polynesian introductions," and those brought in after that date, transported by Europeans or by Polynesians traveling on Western ships or planes, are "modern," "European," or "recent" introductions. Many of the plants used in herbal medicines are native species, but there are sizable minorities of modern and Polynesian introductions. Of the 84 species included here in the text, about 43% are native species, 33% are Polynesian introductions, and 24% are modern introductions. This is almost identical to the results obtained in Tonga (Whistler 1992b) of 44%, 34%, and 23%, respectively.

## LITERATURE ON SAMOAN MEDICINE

There is very little first-hand or even second-hand information on the early practice of Samoan medicine. The first significant accounts were mostly by missionaries, but these were very brief and give the impression that the clergymen were not really familiar with this aspect of Samoan culture. Some recent authors have accused them of overlooking or belittling this important aspect of the ancient Samoan culture because of their religious and Western bias, but whether this is true, and whether or not there was a well-developed system of herbal medicine in pre-European times, may never be known.

The first published mention of specific Samoan herbal remedies was probably by Rev. Thomas Heath, one of the first London Missionary Society missionaries to work in Samoa. Heath (1840) published a brief account of the medical practices he knew, and included specific mention of several plants and their medicinal uses. Another missionary, Rev. Thomas Powell, was in a particularly good position to discuss medicinal plants in Samoa. Powell spent over 30 years in the country and was an amateur botanist. However, his early paper on plant names and uses (Powell 1868) noted medicinal uses (none of which are still practiced) for only about seven species.

At about the same time as Heath, the U.S. Exploring Expedition, led by Capt. Charles Wilkes, visited Samoa, and his account of the expedition (Wilkes 1970, first published in 1845) briefly mentioned some medical practices (but scarcely any of them involving herbal medicines). Other authors in the 1800s noted some Samoan medical practices, most notably the British Consul to Samoa, William Pritchard (1866), and three missionaries—Revs. George Turner (1861), Samuel Ella (1892), and John Stair (1897)—but again, there is little mention in these of herbal medicines. A summary of what was known about Samoan medicine was written by Augustin Krämer in his monumental work called *Die Samoa Inseln* (1902—1903), based mostly on the work of the earlier authors, but Krämer also added 84 remedies (including about 78 plant species) that he recorded directly or indirectly during his work in the islands in the 1890s.

The 20th century brought more observations on herbal medicine. Two botanists who independently made plant collections in Samoa, William Setchell (1924) and Erling Christophersen (1935, 1938), noted the medicinal uses of some of the plants, but did not discuss medical practices (since their research was in botany). At about the same time, Dr. D. Hunt (1923), a medical doctor working on Tutuila in the 1920s, discussed in some detail his impressions of the medical practices at that time, and listed about 43 medicinal plants, but many of these lacked specific uses.

Very little work was done on Samoan medicinal plants for the next half century until two papers on the topic were published in the 1970s. One was a journal article by George Uhe (1974), which listed numerous Samoan medicinal plants, based on interviews with a number of healers and on the previous literature. The other was a discussion of medicinal plants on Tutuila by C. R. (Mick) McCuddin (1974), including a discussion of illnesses and their specific treatment, based upon his interviews with several healers. More recently, Cluny and Sisi Macpherson (1990) discussed the sociological aspects of Samoan medicine, and included several medicinal plant uses. More emphasis was placed on the medicinal plants in *Polynesian Herbal Medicine* (Whistler 1992a), which included a table with 59 Samoan medicinal plants and their uses, based mostly on the literature.

In the last 30 years there have also been a number of scientific articles and books published on various aspects of Samoan medical (but not necessarily herbal medicine) practices. This includes accounts of the treatment of a certain kind of headache called *mo'omo'o* (Crawford 1977), medical incantations (Moyle 1974a), midwives (Kinloch 1985b), beliefs in ghosts (Goodman 1971), the pharmacological testing of plants (Norton *et al.* 1973; Cox *et al.* 1989), birth, pregnancy, and infancy (Niech & Neich 1974), mental health (Clement 1974), health services (Cook 1983; Kinloch 1980, 1985a), the interaction between traditional and Western medicine (Sesepasara 1989), and general accounts (Macpherson 1985; Cox 1990, 1991; Cox and Balick 1994; Elmqvist 1993).

Also of use are Samoan dictionaries. Rev. George Pratt wrote the first significant Samoan dictionary (Pratt 1911), which was first published in 1862 (and revised in 1876, 1892, and 1911). It includes the names of plants and diseases, but does not associate two. A more recent dictionary (Milner 1966) also includes plants and illnesses, but likewise does not associate the two. However, many of the names of Samoan ailments do not appear in these dictionaries, perhaps because the authors did not seek out this specialized information from the appropriate sources—the healers.

# CHAPTER I:
# TRADITIONAL SAMOAN MEDICINE

## THE MEDICAL PROBLEMS

Prior to the arrival of Europeans, the health of the ancient Samoans was generally very good. Because of a long isolation from the rest of the world, infectious diseases such as measles, mumps, and whooping cough were entirely absent. These diseases had long since arrived in Europe, where at first they were very deadly to the population, but over time and several generations became lessened in severity as the survivors passed on some inborn immunity to their offspring. Eventually they became minor ailments that usually occurred in childhood.

Fig. 2. Elephantiasis of the leg caused by filarial worms.

Also noticeably absent were other infectious diseases like smallpox, cholera, typhoid fever, venereal diseases (gonorrhea and syphilis), tuberculosis, influenza, and possibly even the common cold. These diseases were still quite dangerous to Europeans, but even more so to Samoans. The most serious infectious diseases present in Samoa prior to 1830 were yaws (*tona*), elephantiasis (*tupa*) and its cause, filariasis (*mūmū*), and leprosy (*uvi*, a word now replaced by *lepela*). Yaws is a bacterial disease related to syphilis, but is not venereal (i.e., not transmitted by sexual contact).

Filariasis is a disease caused by tiny filarial worms, which are spread by a mosquito vector. The worms concentrate in the lymph system and often cause inflammation (lymphangitis, or inflammation of the lymphatic vessels), chills, fever, headache, and general malaise. In severe and chronic cases, called elephantiasis (Fig. 2), the lymph vessels become obstructed by the worms, leading to permanent swelling of the extremities—the legs, arms, scrotum (in men), and breasts (in women).

In his 1830 diary, Rev. John Williams (Moyle 1974b), first noted the presence of leprosy or Hansen's disease in Samoa:

> "The *oovi* [*ovi*?, which in Pratt is defined as "lumpy"] is also amongst them. This is a frightful disease. The extremities are gradually eaten away till at times the poor unfortunate individual has neither toe or finger

ear or nose left. This is prevalent in all the South Sea Islands with which I am acquainted & for it we know of no cure."

Turner (1861) noted a few decades later that

> "the leprosy of which we speak has greatly abated. The natives say that formerly many had it, and suffered from its ulcerous sores until all the fingers of a hand or the toes of a foot had fallen off."

Other diseases affected Samoans in ancient times. Skin ulcers and infections were certainly present, and probably took up a disproportionate amount of folk healing. Tetanus (*'ona*) from infected cuts and wounds was also a problem. Also present and noted by some of the early published accounts of Samoa were hunchbacks (from a spinal ailment) and eye ailments, such as ophthalmia (inflammation of the eyes), blindness, and pterygium (growth of a membrane across the cornea). Stair (1897) also noted the presence of

> "diseases of the chest and lungs, ...cough, colds, inflammation of the chest and lungs, fevers, rheumatism, pleurisy, diarrhoea, lumbago, diseases of the spine, scrofula...,"

However, many of these may have been foreign ailments, because Stair published his book 67 years after the arrival of the first European missionaries. Ailments of infants, such as thrush, etc., were also undoubtedly present prior to the arrival of the Europeans.

Diseases such as hypertension (*toto maualuga*), diabetes (*ma'i suka*), and cancer (*kanesa*) were probably also present, despite the fact that the names are of European origin. These ailments, the first two of which are, in part, nutritional problems, may have been much less common and were not recognized as distinct illnesses until later. The change in the diet of Samoans from traditional foods to canned Western foods has caused alarming increases in hypertension and diabetes.

## THE CAUSATION OF ILLNESS

Before the advent of Christianity in Samoa, the people believed in many gods (i.e., they were polytheistic). Gods occurred at different levels, and, according to Turner (1861), every village had its own god. Somewhat similar were the spirits, *aitu*, which can perhaps best be equated with "ghosts." Understanding pre-contact Samoan religious practice over 150 years distant now is virtually impossible, for very little has been retained in the oral traditions (since Samoa did not have writing before the arrival of the Europeans), and little was written about the ancient religion by early European authors. The most detailed written accounts were made by the early missionaries, but their descriptions may have been biased because of their firm adherence to Christianity. The best account, and one of the earliest, was by Turner, but a somewhat similar picture is painted by Ella (1892) and Stair (1897).

Ailments affecting the ancient Samoans can be classified into two broad categories, with wounds, burns, rashes, and all other medical problems whose origins were obvious belonging to one group, and ailments occurring within the body and whose origins were not clear belonging to the other. Treatment of the first category may have been largely in the realm of folk medicine, which could be practiced by anyone, while treatment for the second category was handled by specialists, who first had to diagnose the illness and its cause.

The diagnosis of illness is a very difficult process, and even in Western medicine, with all of its modern advances and high technology, the causes of some ailments remain unresolved. In the 19th century, as missionaries were dispensing their medicines in Samoa, Western medicine promoted some beliefs that to us today seem very naive. Stair (1897), for example, noted that some of the health problems were caused by "the all-pervading miasma [gases] arising from the constant decay of rank vegetation."

The ancient Samoans held opinions that now look equally incorrect as we look back through time. Illnesses (i.e., internal ailments) at that time were believed to be caused by gods (*atua*) and spirits (*aitu*), usually as punishment for some transgression against the village, the family, or the gods or spirits. According to Turner (1861),

> "As the Samoans supposed  disease  to be occasioned by the wrath
> of some particular deity, their principal desire, in any difficult case,
> was not for medicine, but to ascertain the cause of the calamity."

Pritchard (1866) noted that

> "All diseases were held to be the visitations of the displeasure of some
> god, and when any one became ill, the first thing done was to consult the
> village priest, and through him to propitiate the offended deity."

Ella (1892) likewise noted that

> "Sickness and death were viewed by the Samoans as proceeding from
> the anger of their tutelary deities, or produced by an evil spirit, or by the
> spirit of a dead relative entering the body of the victim."

All three of these accounts are similar, but it is uncertain whether they are three separate accounts, or if one or both of the latter two were based on the first. However, the lay-healers (*fofō* or *taulāsea*) who do the healing today were not even mentioned by any of the early writers, and it is likely that they did not exist as the distinct class that they are today.

With such beliefs that attribute internal ailments to supernatural powers rather than natural origins, the use of medicinal plants would not have developed, except where it was believed that their application would be obnoxious to the offending spirits and drive them from the body. However, it is not clear to what extent internal medicines were used, since Heath (1840) recorded three remedies that are still employed today.

7

# THE PRIEST-HEALERS

The healing of illness prior to 1830 was in the hands of a priestly class called *taulāitu* ("anchor of the gods"), who were believed to have the power to communicate with the gods. Ella (1892) noted that they were

> "men (sometimes women too) who were supposed to hold intercourse with spirits (the *aitu*). The *taulāitu*, the media of the *aitu* in some points resembled the Roman auguries, and were able to foretell future events. They acted also as the media or intercessors with the totems and tutelary deities, and received the offerings made to such. The office was hereditary and belonged to chiefs in some cases, or members of a particular family, but not limited to these. It was often taken up, or given, on account of some malformation, or from a striking peculiarity in temper or disposition. Hence, many hunchbacks were *taulāitu*, and epileptics, who were considered as possessed of an *aitu*." [The only female *taulāitu* he knew was an epileptic.]

When a person became afflicted with an illness of no obvious origin, the patient was taken to the *taulāitu*, or if this was impractical, the *taulāitu* was summoned to the home of the patient. According to the missionary accounts, these visits would involve payments to the healer to facilitate his intercession with the gods. These payments were considered excessive by early accounts. Turner (1861) noted that

> "The friends of the sick went to the high-priest of the village. He was sure to assign some cause; and, whatever that was, they were all anxiety to have it removed, as the means of restoration. If he said they were to give up a canoe to the god, it was given up. If a piece of land was asked, it was passed over at once."

Pritchard (1866) gave a similar account:

> "For every application, which was always introduced by a present of property or food, the wily priest had a ready answer; he was never at a loss to name the cause of the god's displeasure, and whatever he declared to be the needful propitiation, was promptly offered—and as in the case of childbirth, the god always happened to require something that would be useful to the priest, sometimes it was a canoe, sometimes a piece of land."

The account by Ella (1892) is similar to that by Turner and Pritchard:

> "When a member of a family was seriously ill, messengers would be sent with presents to the priest (*taulāitu*) to inquire the reason of the displeasure of the family god or *aitu*, and to supplicate his clemency and forgiveness.

At such times, the cupidity of the priest would be successfully manifested, and the most valuable property would be demanded and willingly surrendered, as offerings to propitiate the god or *aitu*. The priest would cunningly quote, or invent, some family curse existing, or a case of transgressing against a tabu."

The only descriptions of the actual practice of healing by the *taulāitu* comes from Turner. He described a priestess named Alaiava who served as an intermediary to the god Apelesa, especially in times of birth and serious illness:

"Her usual mode of acting the doctor was, first of all, to order down all the cocoa-nut leaf window-blinds of one end of the house. She then went into the darkened place. Presently that end of the house shook as if by an earthquake, and when she came out she declared what the disease was, and ordered corresponding treatment; the result was that, 'some recovered, and some died'."

Turner described another example of healing by a *taulāitu*, this one serving a god known as Taisumalie:

"His principal remedy was to rub the affected part with oil, and then shout out at the top of his voice five times the word Taisumalie, and five times also call him to come and heal. This being done, the patient was dismissed to wait a recovery."

He further noted that each sickness had its own particular physician.

These descriptions are quite different and difficult to reconcile with each other, but there was probably much individual variation in the practices of the *taulāitu*, which makes categorization difficult. However, the *taulāitu* apparently communicated in some way with the gods, or made it so appear, and asked them to spare his patient. The gods, in turn, would either grant the wish or not, and would possibly communicate the reason why the patient was stricken with the sickness

Other methods of healing used by the *taulāitu* are better documented, since they have parallels to what is used today by the society as a whole or by current healers. One method noted by Turner involved incantations and threats to the god. In treating a disease called *mo'omo'o*, which is a one-sided headache (but described by Turner as "consumption"), there were

"certain doctors who were supposed to be successful in spearing the disease, or, rather, the spirit causing it. The doctor, when sent for, could come in, sit down before the patient, and chant as follows:—'Moomoo e! Moomoo e! o le a ou velosia atu oe;' which in English is:—O moomoo! O Moomoo! I'm on the eve of spearing you. Then he would rise up, flourish about with his spear over the head of the patient, and leave the house. No one dared speak or smile during the ceremony."

A similar method used by laymen was described by Ella:

> "A near relative of the sick one would arm himself with a spear, and pretend to attack the spirit in order to expel it. In the case of sudden death it was said that an *aitu* had devoured the victim."

These descriptions are similar to the methods described by Moyle (1974a) for the modern day treatment of illness by incantations, and to a method demonstrated to the author (in 1995) by one healer, who used a pair of kitchen knives instead of a spear. It also matches a method of treating a type of boil on the head, called *i'atolo*, recorded by the author in 1994 (see p. 30). The other method of healing described by the missionaries is similar to the contemporary use of a healing session within the family. Turner noted that the *taulāitu* would assemble the family:

> "In this ceremony, each member of the family confessed his crimes, and any judgments which, in anger, he had invoked upon the family, or upon the particular member of it then ill, were revoked; and, as proof that he revoked all such imprecations, he took a little water in his mouth, and spurted it out towards the person who was sick. The custom is still kept up by many, and the sick-bed of a dear friend often forms a confessional, before which long-concealed and most revolting crimes are disclosed."

Another practice, this one involving ashes rather than water, was described by Heath (1840):

> "If a man knew that an absent relative or friend was sick, he would take up some ashes into his hand, and looking towards the place where the sick man was residing, would drop the ashes into the other hand."

The meaning of this ritual, and whether it was related to the family healing mentioned above, is unclear.

The description by Turner is strikingly similar to that of Pritchard: the *taulāitu* would

> "require the family to assemble around the bed of the sick relative, and there to confess their sins. The requisition was always implicitly obeyed, and each one confessed everything he or she had ever at any time done. Whether it were theft, adultery, seduction, lying, or invoking a curse upon the sick person, however long concealed, all was openly, and with solemn contrition, confessed; and as evidence of sincerity, a mouthful of water was sprinkled at the bed of the invalid."

These methods are still used in Samoa by the *taulāsea* for curing ailments that they perceive to have a social origin, and a similar therapeutic method called "*ho'oponopono*" is still used in Hawai'i. If relief did not follow the treatment, or if the patient died, the *taulāitu* could blame the family for not being contrite enough, blame the patient who committed the sin, or say that the gods chose not to spare the patient.

## PHYSICAL TREATMENT

The major types of physical treatment of ailments are surgery, treatment of wounds and skin surface ailments, and massage. While it is clear that massage and the treatment of wounds have an ancient tradition in Samoa and elsewhere in Polynesia, surgery has a spotty distribution and level of achievement. Heath (1840) noted that "Scarcely anything is known by the Samoans of surgery, but a few adventures from Tonga and the Fijis have found great practice. The latter are in great repute." Turner (1861) noted that Samoans lanced ulcers with a shell or a shark's tooth, and sometimes used bleeding to treat inflammatory swellings. They also apparently used lancing to reduce pain in some cases. As in Tonga, amputation was virtually never attempted. Stair (1897) noted that

> "If compelled to yield the pride of place as herbalists to the Tongan doctors, the Samoans were fearless and even daring in the use of the knife in disease; whilst in the treatment of broken limbs and wounds received in battle they were most often successful. At times they effected cures under the most unlikely circumstances. From their vegetable diet as well as the constant sea bathing, their flesh seemed to heal more readily than that of others, so that they often survived treatment that would have proved fatal to Europeans. Bullet-wounds, severe contusions, and broken limbs seemed to trouble them but little, unless the wound was given by a blow from a slung stone, which was often very difficult to heal."

Stair went on to describe a particular feat of surgery:

> "I well remember the case of a man, who had been speared in the chest by a jagged spear, which had broken off, leaving several inches in the wound. From the jagged teeth of the spearhead it was impossible to pull it back from the wound; the only alternative, as it appeared to those around, being to force the spearhead and part of the handle through the wound and pull it out on the opposite side. This my informant declared was done; and the man recovered!"

Turner also noted this kind of surgery to remove a spear. Ella (1892), however, noted that "the native surgeons would often perform very rough and barbarous operations." Thus, there is no clear picture of the skill of ancient Samoan surgeons and it is uncertain whether Samoan surgical practices were learned from Tongans and Fijians or independently developed in Samoa. Most likely, 19th century Samoan surgeons rapidly learned their skills in Samoa from Tongans and/or Fijians who had moved to Samoa after the beginning of European contact.

11

Two of the missionaries, Stair and Ella, both noted the use of an autopsy in trying to determine the cause of death of a family member. This was performed by the family itself rather than by an outsider. If a diseased organ or tumor was found, this was removed and burned in hopes that it would not again affect the family. This is similar to the modern practice of burning the core of an infected wound called '*oloā*, which is thought to be caused by the fang of a spirit known as Nifoloa.

The treatment of wounds and skin ailments in Samoa was more advanced in Samoa than it was in Europe, where wounds to the body were almost always fatal. This is principally because of the hygiene practiced by Samoans. Samoans have always valued cleanliness, and wounds were frequently bathed, which reduced the chances of infection. Mariner (Martin 1981) described how the Tongans kept wounds open and draining, but virtually nothing is known about this practice in Samoa. However, in both archipelagoes broken arms were probably immobilized with a temporary cast made out of sections of split coconut frond midribs or the hard spathe that surrounds a coconut palm inflorescence.

The use of massage to heal or soothe ailments was mentioned by Ella, Turner, and Stair, as well as by Wilkes (1970) of the U.S. Exploring Expedition. Unlike their low regard for other types of Samoan healing, the missionaries wrote glowingly of the medical benefits of massage. The most complete description was given by Stair:

> "...a well-known remedy amongst them for easing pain, viz. that which was termed *milimili* ... and *lomilomi*—the first being a gentle rubbing of the head or other parts of the body with the tips of the fingers to ease pain; and the other, a slight pressure or kneading, something after the manner of what is now known as massage. When used skilfully and with a soft hand, either of these remedies was most effectual in relieving pain, whether in the muscles or nerves. The soothing influence of the *milimili* in the case of over-taxed muscles, was most comforting, and must be felt to be appreciated. Gentle friction with the hand and oil was also frequently resorted to with much success; indeed, I think that in many cases these simple remedies were more successful than their efforts with herbs and simples."

Turner added that

> "Shampooing and anointing the affected part of the body with scented oil, by the native doctors, was common; and to this, charms were frequently added, consisting of some flowers from the bush, done up in a piece of native cloth, and put in a conspicuous place in the thatch over the patient."

## HERBAL MEDICINE TREATMENT

There is very little actual information on what extent ancient Samoans used medicinal plants, just a few tantalizing remarks scattered throughout the literature. A much more complete description of medical practices was given for Tonga by Mariner (Martin 1981, first published in 1817) after his stay there from 1806 to 1810. Mariner noted in some detail that the Tongans of that time rarely used medicinal plants, but knew that the Fijians did so extensively. A similar absence of medicinal plant use was noted by Turner (1861) for Samoa:

> "The Samoans, in their heathenism, never had recourse to any internal remedy, except an emetic, which they sometimes tried after having eaten a poisonous fish. Sometimes, juices from the bush were tried; at other times, the patient drank on [sic] at water until it was rejected; and, on some occasions, mud, and even the most unmentionable filth was mixed up and taken as an emetic draught. Laterly, as their recourse with Tongans, Feejeeans, Tahitians, and Sandwich Islanders increased, they made additions to their pharmacopoeia of juices from the bush."

Stair (1897) similarly described the early medicinal practices, and, interestingly enough, by this time (his work was published 80 years after that of Mariner) attributes medicinal plant use to Tongan immigrants:

> "Although they [the Samoans] had much sickness their remedies were few, and for the most part unreliable, notwithstanding the fact that the flora of the group included many medicinal plants and herbs of much value...Of native doctors, strictly speaking, the best obtainable were the Tongan doctors, many of whom were found on Samoa. These men had a better knowledge of the native herbs and plants than the Samoans themselves. Still, there were many Samoans who followed this particular employment .... I have been informed of instances that have come under the observation of others in which very powerful and drastic herbs and plants have been used, apparently without any idea of their caustic nature."

Ella (1892) generally concurred in his brief mention of medicinal plants:

> "The Tongan doctors, a large number of whom found a remunerative practice in Samoa, employed medicines—chiefly decoctions of herbs, often very successfully, in acute diseases."

A somewhat contradictory picture was painted by Heath (1840), who noted that "The Samoans, however, were not entirely destitute of skill and resources. Many trees & etc. were in use by them." He went on to note about seven medicinal uses of plants, the most interesting of which was the use of bamboo ash for treating burns, which is a common folk remedy today. However, the remedies of Heath appear to be mostly, or perhaps entirely, external applications.

It thus appears that prior to the advent of Europeans into Samoa, most of the healing was by massage, incantations, and consultations with the gods believed to be responsible for the illness. Medicinal plants were not a major component of healing, at least not for internal remedies. The medicines taken internally may have been mostly purgatives, or served to repel *aitu* that were thought to be causing sickness or impeding recovery. But external applications were undoubtedly used, some of which are still employed today. The use of external applications was noted by Turner: "With the exception of external applications for skin diseases, they had no remedies for the numerous disorders of children." He also noted that cuts were washed in the sea and bound with a leaf, presumably a medicinal leaf. Both Heath and Turner noted the use of the smoke of burning **ifi** (Tahitian chestnut, *Inocarpus fagifer*) wood for treating wounds, a remedy no longer practiced.

What is not mentioned by any of the authors, however, is the role of women in treating infants. There may be a variety of possible reasons for this, perhaps the likeliest of which is that the men who wrote these passages were not familiar with the role of women in healing infants. However, it is likely that medicinal plants were used for ailments of infancy, especially because some remedies used for infants are found in both western and eastern Polynesia, which were isolated from each other for perhaps 1800 years before the European Era in Polynesia.

## THE TRANSITION PERIOD

Because in ancient Samoan society the causes of illness were rooted in Samoan religion, these beliefs had to undergo drastic changes when the gods of the old Samoan religion were banished by the arriving Christian missionaries. When the gods were disgraced, so too was their perceived ability to cause disease. The priest-healers lost power in both the religious field as well as the medicinal field. Consequently, a new set of beliefs developed that accepted natural causes for ailments, and natural medicines to cure them, fortified by the healers' belief in God.

The new beliefs were also promoted by the course of events that followed the establishment of the Christian churches in Samoa, most notably the series of epidemics that swept over Samoa, killing thousands of susceptible victims each time a scourge visited the islands.

The first reported epidemic (perhaps cholera) preceded the missionaries (in an unknown year) to Samoa and caused great loss of life. In 1830, at about the same time of the landing of Rev. John Williams, influenza swept through the islands killing hundreds and perhaps thousands. Turner (1861) noted that the disease thereafter returned almost annually, each time taking additional lives and depopulating the islands. Particularly virulent attacks occurred in 1837 and 1846. In 1849, whooping cough made its first appearance, killing adults as well as children. Two years later it was the mumps, which again killed both adults and children, and affected nearly the whole population. Smallpox, the dreaded killer throughout the world, apparently never caused an epidemic in Samoa, probably due to the vaccination of virtually the entire population by the missionaries. But other severe epidemics continued to arrive, the worst of which was probably the great influenza epidemic that swept the world in 1918.

These epidemics had a drastic effect on the population, which plummeted, as well as on the survivors and Samoan society. They were seen to be *Pālagi* (foreign) diseases, which could not be treated by traditional means. They were, however, treated by the missionaries with some degree of success, as were other ailments. If *Pālagi* illnesses were treated with medicines by the Westerners, why then could not Samoan illnesses be treated by Samoan medicines (i.e., herbal medicines from local plants)?

These factors—the loss of traditional religion, the series of epidemics, and the examples of using internal medicines set by the missionaries—are the most likely origins for the extensive use of herbal medicines in Samoan medicine today. There was probably a period of great experimentation during the last half of the 19th century, but eventually some of the medicines became standardized and the use of others disappeared when they proved to be ineffective.

On Powell's list of plant names published in 1868, only about seven are recorded with medicinal uses, and none of these are in current usage. Krämer (1902—1903) recorded 84 remedies before 1900, most of which are no longer in use today. Also of note is that about two-thirds of these pre-1900 remedies included more than one species of plant, whereas today perhaps 90% of herbal remedies involve only a single plant species, and rarely more than two or three.

Hunt (1923) recorded about 43 medicinal plants used on Tutuila in the early 1920s, and although 28 of these are among the 84 listed in this book, less than a quarter of the specific uses recorded are the same as practiced today. Christophersen (1935, 1938) included over a dozen plants that he noted as medicinal, and most of the specific medicinal uses are still practiced, or were until recently.

So it appears that sometime between the late 19th century and the early 20th century, Samoan medicine as we now know it was established and standardized to some degree. It is not clear, however, how the *fofō*, who are the healers of today, came to their present position. They do not seem to have evolved from the *taulāitu*, who were mostly men of the priestly class. Perhaps their position evolved from women who always tended to the medical needs of children in the family, and were apparently unnoticed by the authors of the 19th century.

With this rise in herbal medicines, the *taulāitu* probably just faded away. However, Hunt (1923) gave a description of how some of them were still operating in the 1920s:

> "The modus operandi in one case is for the "devil" doctor to enter the house of the sick person with a coconut shell containing smoking ashes; he passes around the sick person blowing the smoke toward the patient and uttering a few mumbled words. Another method consists of touching the supposedly sick part or the sick person with a coconut palm and making a circular motion with the palm. This circular motion is increased by one for each time the patient is treated. The most popular treatment is called 'chasing the devil.' A dose of some poison is first administered, usually the sap of *Barringtonia speciosa* [*B. asiatica*, **futu**]. About the time the effect of the poison is to be noticed, the 'devil' doctor enters with four assistants who have a sheet or similar cloth, which is spread out and held about 2 feet above the floor. The 'devil' doctor beats the patient

with his hands until the occurrence of convulsions. The first cockroach, moth, or insect that falls into the sheet is supposed to be the devil. The sheet is immediately closed over the supposed devil, which is taken outside and killed. The convulsions of the patient are caused by the devil trying to get out. If the patient recovers from the poison, he is supposed to be rid of this particular devil. In event of a fatal outcome the 'devil' doctor is already with the excuse that death could not have been caused by a devil, because the devil was captured and destroyed, but was punishment by the Almighty God for theft. Usually all the thefts that had occurred in the village during the past few weeks are blamed on the dead one."

Although new medicinal plants are constantly being added, by the 1930s most of the uses had become somewhat standardized and recognizable today, particularly in the prevalence of single-plant medicines. The practice of medicine, such as the diagnosis of sickness and preparation of medicines, has probably remained basically unchanged since the 1920s. Most of the healers learned their medicines from an older relative with little change, taking the currently used remedies back at least two generations.

# CHAPTER II.
# MODERN SAMOAN MEDICINE

## HEALTH CARE IN SAMOA TODAY

Two systems of health care exist side by side in Samoa—Samoan medicine and Western medicine. Western medicine is centered in three hospitals—Moto'otua Hospital near Apia, Tuasivi Hospital on Savai'i, and the Lyndon B. Johnson Tropical Medical Center in American Samoa. There are also a series of rural clinics, especially on Savai'i, that are staffed by district nurses. The doctors (*foma'i*) at the Western Samoan hospitals have either a Diploma of Medicine from the Fiji School of Medicine or an M.D. from New Zealand or elsewhere, and there are usually a few *Pālagi* (Western) M.D.s and interns from overseas who work along with them. The doctors in American Samoa are M.D.s from the U.S. or elsewhere, and serve on contract for two or more years.

In most of the world, Western medicine has demonstrated its superiority over indigenous medical practices, but this is not the case in Samoa, at least not for all ailments. The first line of defense for many Samoans, particularly for infants, is Samoan medicine. This is not due to isolation, because most districts have a clinic, and the majority of the population is less than an hour's bus or car ride from one of the three hospitals noted above. However, a clinic staffed by a nurse is not the same as a hospital staffed by doctors and medical equipment. Savai'i is particularly weak in this area, since the one hospital is now (1994) being rebuilt, and often there are no more than two doctors for the entire island.

The two systems are in direct competition, but there is very little conflict or tension. The doctors may think of the *fofō*—the traditional healers—as "witch doctors," and the *fofō* may confidently believe that the Western doctors just do not have the power to heal Samoan ailments, but there is little friction. *Fofō* recognize a dichotomy in ailments, with some classified as Samoan illnesses (*ma'i Sāmoa*) and others as Western illnesses (*ma'i Pālagi*). They usually treat only the former type, which they consider indigenous; if the *fofō* determine that the illness of a prospective patient belongs to the latter type, which is considered to be introduced by Westerners, and they do not have a medicine to treat it, the patient will be directed to a hospital or clinic. Likewise, some Western doctors may send patients to *fofō* if they believe that the ailment is not readily treatable with Western medicines or is psychological and is best treated by traditional Samoan means. However, referral from doctor to *fofō* is less common than the reverse.

Instead of open friction, there is mutual tolerance and even some cooperation between the two systems. In its village public health programs, the Western Samoan Health Department has sought out village women (women's committee members), some of them being established *fofō*. The health department representatives—the district nurses living and working in the village—may even believe in Samoan medicine; even if they do not, they may refrain from condemning the practice in order to maintain harmony with their patients and village. The Health Department has even officially recognized some of the *fofō*, and supplies them with items such as gauze for use in the preparation of Samoan medicine. This may be an attempt to westernize Samoan medicine,

Fig. 3.(T,L)  Medicinal leaves are stacked in the hand.    Fig. 4. (T,R)   The leaves are rolled.
Fig. 5. (B,L)  The crushed leaves. Fig. 6. (B,R) The juice of the crushed leaves is dripped onto
a cut.

18

but on the other hand, it may confer legitimacy to Samoan medicine in the eyes of the healers and people.

Samoan medicine itself can be divided into two basic types: one practiced by the traditional healers, the *fofō*, the other by untrained individuals and known as folk medicine. Folk medicine is based upon a body of common knowledge, such as first aid, massage, and properties of medicinal plants, that is shared by the community. Everyone knows that if you cut yourself while working in the plantation, you rub the leaves of **fue Saina** (mile-a-minute weed, *Mikania micrantha*) in your hands (Fig. 3—6) and drip the juice onto the wound to staunch the bleeding and prevent infection. Everyone also knows that you drip the juice of **lā'au fai lafa** (candlebush, *Senna alata*) onto ringworm infections of the skin. Likewise, most people know that burns can be treated by applying ashes of the leaves of **'ofe** (Polynesian bamboo, *Schizostachyum glaucifolium*) mixed with coconut oil. These medicinal applications, and others like them, are folk remedies that do not require the services of a *fofō*, because the medicine is not "proprietary" or owned by anyone.

However, if the ailment is more complicated, or is a chronic rather than a first-aid problem, and more expert diagnosis and treatment is needed, then a *fofō* is consulted. These two categories of Samoan medicine are not always distinct, however. Some healers have personal remedies that are identical to what others practice as folk medicine. Most women know a few medicinal plants for treating their babies, such as applying the yellow powder (*lega*) from the **ago** plant (turmeric, *Curcuma longa*) mixed with coconut oil to mouth sores (*'atiloto*). A woman may treat her own baby with this remedy as a folk medicine, or the remedy may be owned. When she treats other children, especially children outside her own family, she then is considered a *fofō*; if this is her only remedy, however, then the distinction is not very clear.

## CONCEPTS OF SICKNESS AND HEALTH

Although most of the ancient concepts of the effects of gods (*atua*) and spirits or ghosts (*aitu*) in causing disease were lost or became obsolete, some other traditional concepts have continued to be held by the culture, especially in the spiritual and social realms. Even today, the importance of social relationships in Samoa cannot be overstated. Every individual is part of a well-defined social group or extended family, which includes even distant relatives. Also included are ancestors, who are believed by many to interact with the living as spirits (*aitu*). Along with the strong sense of belonging to this social unit is the strong sense of obligation (*tiuti*) to the family. To fail to fulfill these obligations can lead to disharmony in the family.

Macpherson and Macpherson (1990) pointed out that Samoan culture traditionally places the individual in three 'worlds'—a natural world, a social world, and a spiritual world—and that people are constantly influenced by the relationship between themselves and these three worlds. A state of good health, or *soifua maloloina*, is achieved by maintaining a balance in the three worlds and avoiding tensions. However, this ideal condition often fails, as the balance is rarely perfect. Too much tension and imbalance in the three worlds can lead to an illness with a non-natural origin, and the healer must treat the patient accordingly. *Aitu* are still believed to cause some diseases and retard

19

healing in others, but God Himself is not generally believed to cause illness, with the exception of some ailments called *ma'i agasala* that are believed to result from the sufferer's violation of moral law.

If the healer determines that the illness is in the natural world (i.e., it appears to be physical in origin), then treatment with herbal medicines, changes in diet, or changes in lifestyle may be recommended. The connection between the increasing consumption of *Pālagi* food instead of Samoan food and the increasing incidence of hypertension and diabetes is generally recognized, but hard to cure. If the ailment the healer is treating has a non-natural origin (i.e., a psychological or supernatural origin), then treatment may involve family counseling, family meetings to air out differences, or treatment for a supernaturally induced ailment.

There is also the belief that some illnesses are caused by the positions of internal organs, especially the *to'ala* discussed below. The misalignment of the organs is thought to cause symptoms such as backaches and others pains, much as Western chiropractors attribute illness to the alignment of the spine. Some ailments are believed to be caused by the accumulation of harmful substances in the body, which must be removed by medicines, particularly by purgatives. The traditional and current use of purgatives and laxatives in Samoa, however, is not so pronounced as it was in much of eastern Polynesia, where these were traditionally administered after nearly all internal medicines. The choice of medicines to use in the case of sickness is directed by God, and even if there is no clear understanding of how the plants themselves effect their cure, healers do not generally feel a need to question any further.

# SAMOAN AILMENTS

It is difficult to categorize all ailments present in Samoa, or even those treated by means of traditional medicine. However, there is a need to explain what is being treated by the herbal medicines, and this requires some classification and categorization. The following is an attempt to do this. The three major divisions recognized here are Surface Ailments, Internal Ailments, and Supernaturally Induced Ailments. The surface ailments are further divided into five groups: 1. Boils; 2. Skin Sores and Rashes; 3. Inflammation; 4. Wounds and Burns; and 5. Eye Ailments. The Internal Ailments are divided into seven groups: 1. Mouth and Throat Infections; 2. Digestive Tract Ailments; 3. Internal Organ Ailments; 4. Women's Ailments; 5. Ailments of Newborn Infants; 6. Physical Injury; and 7. Foreign (*Pālagi*) Ailments. The Supernaturally Induced Ailments are divided into two groups: (1) Possession (*Ma'i Aitu*); and 2. Hard-to-Cure Ailments (*Sāua*).

## Surface Ailments
### 1. Boils

With a warm and humid climate like Samoa's, the incidence of boils and carbuncles (a deep-seated boil usually with more than one head) is high. Another contributing factor is the diet of Samoans, which is generally poor in vitamins. Although boils have similar origins—bacterial infections of the skin, often of a hair follicle—they are given different names in Samoa, based upon their severity and their location on the body. A boil that develops on the arms or legs is usually called a *ma'i sua* (literally, "flowing sickness"). When it occurs on the upper body (i.e., the back, stomach, abdomen, etc.), it is called *sila'ilagi*, which is a cognate of the Tongan name *hila'akilangi* for the same ailment. A boil occurring on the lower body, especially on the buttocks, near the anus, or on the genitals, is called a *sila'ilalo*, a cognate of the Tongan name *hila'akilalo*. A boil occurring in the armpit is called a *lo'omatua* (literally, "old woman"). Pratt (1911), however, called this *tama'ita'i* (literally, "young woman").

The most common treatment for boils involves crushing the leaves of several species of plants and applying them to the boil, with or without the use of scented coconut oil called "Samoan oil." The most commonly used species for this are **'aute Samoa** (red hibiscus, *Hibiscus rosa-sinensis*) and **polo feū** (chili pepper, *Capsicum frutescens*). The latter plant is an introduced species that may have replaced other species of **polo** belonging to the same family (Solanaceae, the nightshade family). An alphabetical listing of Samoan plant names, with their scientific names, is found in Chapter III.

Several other types of skin ailments are similar to boils. An infection of a sebaceous gland on the eyelid is a *matafā* (sty). It is commonly treated with flowers and leaves of **nonu** (Indian mulberry, *Morinda citrifolia*). *Fuafua* are pimples. *I'atolo* is a condition in which many small boils or sores occur on the scalp. *'Oloā* is a type of infected wound or boil that is usually thought to be of supernatural origin, and is discussed further under that category below. However, some types of *'oloā* are thought to have natural origins, such as *'oloā sami* (literally *'oloā* "from the sea"). This may be an infected puncture wound, such as from a sea urchin spine, but it may also be caused by a puncture wound occurring on land. Another similar ailment, *fāoailetā*, is a general term for septicemia ("blood poisoning"), but is often manifested by a sore on the soles of the feet. Another ailment perhaps best fitting in this category is tetanus, called *'ona* in Samoan. Tetanus is a toxic bacterial infection of muscles resulting from a wound from a sharp object that was in contact with the soil where the particular pathogenic bacteria live.

2. Skin Sores and Rashes

Skin sores or skin ulcers are superficially similar to boils, but are usually restricted to the skin surface rather than being deeply rooted. Many kinds are recognized by Samoan healers, some of which do not have any precise definition in Western medicine. They are particularly common in the hot, humid climate of Samoa, and may result from small cuts or mosquito bites. The term most commonly used collectively to refer to skin sores, especially when they occur in large numbers, is *papala*, which is very similar to the term for stomatitis or mouth sores, *pala*. The general term for a sore is *po'u*; a variation of this sometimes recognized is *po'u sā*, which reportedly leaves permanent white blotches on the skin, and is, or is identical or similar to impetigo. The most common plants used to treat skin sores are **ago**, **leva**, **pate**, and **seasea**.

Another skin disease is *tona* (yaws), a bacterial disease related to syphilis but not sexually transmitted nor as serious, and characterized by crusted ulcers on the skin of the limbs. It was once nearly universally present in Samoa, but the first infection conferred immunity from further attacks (it also conferred immunity from syphilis, which was, however, not present in Samoa prior to the arrival of the Europeans). Yaws has now been eliminated from Samoa by the concerted application of antibiotics, but treatments for the ailment are still remembered by some healers, typically the application of the crushed stems of **limu** (*Ramalina* sp.), a lichen.

Another ailment, *manemane* (sometimes spelled *magemage*), was defined by Pratt (1911) as "a disease that eats away the skin of the palms of the hands and soles of the feet." Sores around the mouth or lips, termed erysipelas, are called in Samoan *'atiloto*, although some sources define this instead as shingles, a viral disease (*Herpes zoster*) marked by skin eruptions extending in a line from the spinal cord. Another disease that may belong here, *foe*, is described as growths on a baby's scalp.

There are also a number of skin sores or rashes caused by fungi. The best known of these is ringworm, *lafa*, which apparently was not present in Samoa prior to the European Era. It is commonly treated by the introduced candlebush plant (*Senna alata*), which is called **lā'au fai lafa**. This folk remedy appears to be effective because of the presence of prussic acid in the leaves. Another common skin fungus is *tane* (*Tinea versicolor*), which is characterized by large, irregular blotches on the skin. Several types of *tane* are recognized, based upon the color of the infection. Another fungal skin infection called *'utu* is sometimes confused with lice, which are called by the same name.

The general term for rash or itchiness is *mageso*. Diaper rash of infants is called *mū* (the same word for burns). Warts, called *lafitoga* in Samoa, are caused by a virus under the skin. One treatment recognized by Pratt for treating warts was called **limu**, which was described as applying **limu** (a lichen, possibly *Ramalina* sp.) to warts. Possibly related to these ailments is *matolo*, defined as a large blister on the scalp. The latter has traditionally been treated by using the plant called **lau i'atolo** (*Stephania forsteri*), but this species is rare now and the remedy infrequently used.

## 3. Inflammation

Inflammation (*mūmū*) is included here under surface ailments, but in addition to inflammation of the superficial skin tissue and visible discoloration of the skin, it also includes elevated body temperature. The treatment of inflammation is a major part of Samoan herbal medicine, and several ailments are collectively included in this category. Originally, *mūmū* also referred to the effects of filariasis, but this disease has virtually been eliminated from Samoa.

Some *mūmū* ailments are minor and not life-threatening, while others are serious and potentially fatal. Heath (1973) recorded eleven types and a nearly equal number were recorded during the interviews for this book. However, there is little standardization in this aspect of Samoan medicinal terminology, and the various definitions obtained during the interviews confirm that not all names always refer to the same ailments among the healers. Some types of *mūmū* are specific to one body region, while others can occur anywhere on the body.

The most common or best known types of *mūmū* are the following: (1) *mūmū asuafi*, characterized by blisters that ooze and spread, and perhaps is scabies; (2) *mūmū lele*, which may be blood poisoning from an infected wound, and is a serious ailment; (3) *mūmū lili*, an ailment of infants characterized by fever, dizziness, and seizures; (4) *mūmū melo*, characterized by inflammation, especially around the anus of infants; (5) *mūmū sāua*, which involves chills and headache, and is thought to have a supernatural origin; (6) *mūmū ta'ai*, characterized by fever and difficulty in breathing; (7) *mūmū tatau*, characterized by the discoloration of the skin of babies, something like a tattoo (*tatau*); (8) *mūmū tua'ula*, characterized by red skin blotches, fever, and sleeplessness; (9) *mumu tua'ula uli*, characterized by fever and discoloration of the soles of the feet.

Inflammation is one of the most common ailments treated by Samoan herbal medicine, and numerous plants are employed, most commonly **nonu, matalafi, fue sina, aloalo vao** (especially for *mūmū tatau*), **lau tī** (the leaf is used for massage), **lau mafiafia, aloalo, pua Sāmoa, togo, lau 'autā**, and **ma'anunu** (mostly for *mūmū tua'ula*). The first three plants are probably used mostly for inflammations thought to have a supernatural origin.

The general term for swelling is *fula*, which is a common ailment in Samoa. One kind of swelling that is not classified as *fula* is *tupa*, which is the permanent swelling of the limbs caused by filarial worms (see Fig. 2); however, filariasis has now been virtually eliminated from Samoa. One of the plants most commonly used for treating swelling is **nonu**, probably when the origin of the swelling is unknown and feared to be supernatural. Also used for this purpose are **'ava'avaaitu tū, matalafi, gatae**, and **tagitagi**. The first two species, like **nonu**, are often associated with supernaturally-induced ailments.

## 4. Wounds and Burns

Wounds have always been a part of Samoan culture, and there have been herbal treatments for them since ancient times. The general word for wound is *lavea* or *manu'a*. Two problems are caused by wounds—the immediate bleeding and the long term effects of the breaching of the skin, which allows pathogens to enter and cause infection. Several plants are commonly applied to cuts—the leaves of **fue Saina**, and the sap of **fu'afu'a, mautofu**, and **aloe** (spelled like its English name, but pronounced "ah-loy"). Two of the four are introduced species. **Aloe** is a very recent introduction that has rapidly gained popularity for treating cuts and burns. Two other species were probably used in the past, but are infrequently employed now. **Mamala**, apparently called **fanuamamala** or **fogāmamala** in the past, and **lau tamatama** were applied to circumcision wounds. However, since circumcision is now done under more hygienic conditions, and because **lau tamatama** (*Achyranthes aspera*) is now very uncommon, these usages have largely been forgotten.

Burns are also very common in Samoa, since open fires are still often used to cook food, frequently in open cookhouses where the fire and hot pots are easily accessible to young children. The most common treatment for burns is Polynesian bamboo (**'ofe**), the only medicinal plant recorded in Samoa whose ashes are used rather than the fresh leaves. Over the last two decades **aloe** has become increasingly popular for the treatment of burns, as it has in the Western world.

Similar to wounds and burns are insect stings, and puncture wounds from the spines of fish. The only stinging or biting insects in Samoa are ants (*loata*, whose bite is only painful for a short time), bees and wasps (*pī*), which are introduced, and centipedes (*atualoa*), which are native. There are several poisonous fish in the sea, the worst of which is the stingray (*fai*) and the stonefish (*gofu*), which can inflict serious wounds. Being stung by a poisonous fish is called *tuia*. There are no commonly recognized treatments for these stings, except for the use of **fue Saina** in treating bee and wasp stings.

## 5. Eye Ailments

Several types of eye ailments are recognized in Samoa, some caused by trauma, some by infections, and some by natural aging processes. The general term for these ailments is *ma'i mata*, defined simply as "eye ailment." One of the most common infectious ailments is *matafā* (sty), which is a boil on the eyelid; it is described above in the section on boils. Another type of infection is *fuafua lili'i*, which is described as numerous small pimples suddenly appearing around the eye and accompanied by pain. Another ailment that appears in cycles and infects large numbers of people throughout the country before it disappears as suddenly as it appears is "pink eye" (conjunctivitis).

Injury or trauma to the eye is called *mata pa'ia*, and can be caused by a foreign object poking the eye, or a piece of dirt or sawdust being lodged in it. *Mata māsae* is another type of injury, literally "torn eye," which involves pain and the discharge of fluid. The term *ogoogo* (or *ogo*) refers to eye irritation, or sore eyes, perhaps from being exposed to too much wind or sun. Another ailment, *mata 'avea* is blurry vision, possibly caused by a person spending too much time outside in the evening when *aitu* are more likely to be out and about.

Two ailments involve abnormal growths on the eye. One is called *tū* (pterygium), a growth across the cornea of the eye. Another term, *moālili*, a white membrane that forms over the eye, was defined by Macpherson and Macpherson (1990) as corneal scars in the eye, and may be the same as *tū*. Cataracts (*una'i'a*) are another problem, particularly of older people. The plants most commonly used for treating eye ailments are **gatae** (sap from the petiole), **nonu** (sties are treated with the flowers and leaf stalks), **togo** (leaves), **'ulu** (the sap from the petiole), **a'atasi** (whole plant), **ogoogo tea** (whole plant), **'o'a** (leaves), **fau** (sap from the bark), and **fu'afu'a** (sap from the bark).

## Internal Ailments

The division of ailments into internal and external is somewhat artificial, since ailments like mouth infections may be considered external by Western doctors but internal by Samoan healers. However, as used here, "internal ailments" includes all ailments of the digestive tract and several other general medical problems.

## 1. Mouth and Throat Infections

Infections of the mouth (stomatitis) are probably the most common ailments treated by Samoan healers. Babies are particularly susceptible to these ailments since their bodies have not yet built up immunity to many of the childhood diseases. The general

24

term for mouth and throat infections is *pala*. When mouth infections are specifically meant, the term *pala gutu* is used. Another commonly used term is *pala fefie*, which is stomatitis with swollen and bleeding gums.

Two kinds of fungal infections are distinguished, one or both of which may correspond to thrush: *eaea* and *eaea sā*, which are characterized by a white coating of the mouth, lips and tongue. Another commonly mentioned ailment is *gutu malū*, literally "soft mouth," which Macpherson and Macpherson (1990) noted was usually caused by burns from hot food, and may loosely be translated as mouth sores. *Fa'a'ī tīgā* (sore throat) is also common, particularly during colds. A runny nose is called *isu mamafa*, literally "heavy nose," and a cough is *tale*.

Stomatitis and its related ailments are usually treated with potions made from tree bark, some of which act as an emetic to clear out the mouth and respiratory system. The most commonly used plants for *pala gutu* are **moegālō**, **mago**, **nonu fi'afi'a**, **fue manogi**, **ago**, **milo**, **vī**, **'o'a**, **lama**, **masame**, **nonu**, and **talie**.

## 2. Digestive Tract Ailments

Illnesses affecting the stomach and intestines are also common in Samoa, but are usually of short duration. The manifestations of these ailments can be stomach pain, gassy stomach, diarrhea, dysentery, constipation, and intestinal pain. Some of these ailments are diagnosed by the condition of the feces.

The general term for ailments of the lower digestive tract is *pala ga'au*, but this may sometimes specifically refer to stomach ulcers. The general term for stomach problems is *ma'i manava*, literally "sickness of the stomach." Stomach pain is *manava tīgā*, and gassy stomach is *manava fefete* ("swollen stomach"). Rapid and suddenly appearing stomach pain is called *manava oso* ("jumping stomach"). One well-known stomach ailment, *osofā punimoa*, is apparently blockage of the entrance to the stomach, thus preventing food from entering. This is sometimes attributed to the *to'ala* (see under the next section) pressing up against the stomach entrance. Upset stomach is sometimes accompanied by vomiting (*pua'i*) and some remedies for chest congestion encourage this (i.e., they are meant to be emetics).

The word for diarrhea is *manava tatā* (also commonly called *muli sī*), but several names are recognized. In *tulatula*, the stools have white or yellow deposits. If blood is present in the stools (i.e., dysentery), the term used is *sagatoto*. Another related word is *filogia*, which is blood in the stools (or urine) caused by a bleeding ulcer or other source in the digestive tract. Constipation is generally called *manava mamau*. In one variation of this, called *fe'efe'e*, the stools are black. Intestinal worms (*'anufe*) sometimes infect Samoans, but this is not a major problem, and there seems to be no general remedy for their treatment in Samoan herbal medicine. Hookworms are called *'anufe matau*, which is a direct translation of the English term.

The most commonly used plants for treating stomach ailments are **fiu** (ginger) and **ku'ava** (guava). Both of these plants are European introductions, and the use of the latter for treating stomach ailments is known throughout the Pacific Islands. **Moso'oi** bark is sometimes used as a purgative (*vai fa'atafe*).

## 3. Internal Organ Ailments

The distinction between this category and ailments of the digestive tract is not always clear, since many of the internal organs are directly connected to it. Respiratory diseases are common in Samoa, some of them a minor inconvenience but others life threatening. The treatment of respiratory difficulties (*sela*), sometimes identified as asthma, is a common remedy in the repertoire of Samoan healers. Tuberculosis (*māmāpala*) is commonly treated at the hospitals, since it is *ma'i Pālagi* (foreign sickness). Another *ma'i Pālagi* is flu, called *fulū*, which is a transliteration of the English word "flu." It also includes the common cold, which is often similar to the flu. A serious case is called *fulū gau*. A related ailment, a flu-like sickness that gets worse, is called *ma'i gau*. The most frequently used plants for treating respiratory difficulties are **fiu** (ginger) and **namulega**.

The liver is called *ate*, and ailments of it are generally called *ma'i ate* (apparently called *aupā* in American Samoa). One specific type, which appears to be a swollen liver and jaundice, is called *ate fefete*, but there is no widely used medicinal plant for treating this.

One of the most troublesome of the organ systems is the urinary tract—the kidneys, bladder, and urethra. The general term for urinary tract problems is *tulitā*, but a number of specific types are recognized. Difficult urination is called *tulitā mamau*, and painful urination is *tulitā fasia* (or perhaps the same thing, *tulitā tīgā*). These often are urinary tract infections, some of which are believed to be caused by evil spirits, and are called *tulitā sāua*. Gonorrhea and other venereal diseases are called *ma'i afi* ("fire sickness"), and neither it nor *saga vai*, incessant urination, perhaps diabetes insipidus, is included in the *tulitā* category. Some kinds of *tulitā* do not seem to be urinary tract problems at all. *Tulitā filēmū*, "gentle urinary tract problem," appears to be some kind of diarrhea that leads to weight loss. The most commonly used medicinal plant for urinary tract ailments is **ateate**. Less frequently used plants include **fasa**, **lau 'autā**, and **mamala**.

Another ailment that should probably be included in this category is called *to'ala*, sometimes spelled and pronounced *to'oala*. There is considerable disagreement over exactly what this is. Some people believe that the *to'ala* (which refers to the organ and the ailment) is an organ like the uterus that only occurs in women, but most healers believe it to be an organ found in both women and men. It is commonly conceived of as octopus-like in shape, residing near the solar plexus of the abdomen and adhering to internal organs by tentacle-like attachments. Sometimes, however, it moves from this spot to other parts of the body, causing pain. Symptoms include lower back and joint pain, constipation, and dark colored-urine. The medicines and massage used to treat *to'ala* ailments are for the purpose of returning the *to'ala* to its correct position. The same or similar ailment is recognized in Tonga and Tokelau (called *toka'ala* in both places), and seems to be an ancient concept shared throughout western Polynesia.

## 4. Women's Ailments

Being the bearers of children, women are susceptible to a number of ailments exclusive to them. Most of these are directly related to the reproductive tract and childbirth. Many of these ailments are related to menstruation (*ma'i masina*, literally, "monthly sickness"). One ailment, menorrhagia (excessive or prolonged menstrual flow), is called *punatoto* or its equivalent, *piliki* ("bleeding"), and is common to women throughout the world. Infertility, *fafine lē fananau*, is recognized as an ailment and is treated by some healers, principally through the use of massage.

The most commonly treated ailment of women, however, appears to be *failele gau,* postpartum relapse sickness, in which the new mother is slow in recovering from, or starts normal activities too soon after, giving birth. The most commonly used remedies for *failele gau* include the leaves of **fisoa**, a shrub that grows on the beach. Also occasionally used are the bark of **moli 'aina, milo**, and **pu'a**.

### 5. Ailments of Newborn Infants

This category includes ailments that affect only infants, but many of these are listed under internal ailments, such as stomatitis, thrush, etc., which almost exclusively affect infants and children and could just as well have been placed here. The most common of the neonatal ailments belong to a category called *ila*. This is undoubtedly an ancient concept or grouping of neonatal ailments, since the same name or cognates of it are found in Tahiti, the Cook Islands, Tonga, and elsewhere in Polynesia. It has sometimes been simply defined as "birthmark," which is one of its meanings, but the concept of *ila* being a broad category of ailments of children is the one adhered to by Samoan healers. Some of the various ailments appear to have little in common other than their appearance in infants.

One of the most common is *ila fale*, a term also used in Tonga. It seems to be some kind of irritability of the baby, possibly caused by its being away from home or familiar surroundings; *fale* is the word for house. Another well-known type is *ila mea*, which appears to be diaper rash, perhaps an inflammation around the anus caused by diarrhea. Other types of *ila* include *ila toso* and *ila fa'a'autama*, which are difficult to define or characterize.

The plants most commonly used for treating the different kinds of *ila* are **a'atasi**, **togo**, and **ufi**, all of them small prostrate herbs, which may have significance (baby plants?). Less commonly used are the sap of **fa'i**, the sap and leaves of **lau 'autā**, and the juice from a coconut husk. In one unusual treatment, the smoke from a burning breadfruit stick is used (see **'ulu** in Chapter III for more details).

Another commonly used term referring to an ailment of a baby is *la'ofia* or *lanuia*, which is meconium aspiration—the swallowing by the fetus of its own wastes (meconium) in the amniotic fluid before birth, causing congestion of the respiratory system. If the ingested meconium is not cleaned out just after birth, it is believed that harm may occur later in life. It is commonly treated with the juice of a coconut husk, or with the chewed pulp of sugar cane. Teething (*nifoa*) is another ailment of babies, as is *'ōnā*, which is sickness in a baby who is still breast-feeding when the mother becomes pregnant again. Samoans believe that the breast milk becomes "poisonous" (*'ōnā*) to an infant when the mother becomes pregnant again.

## 6. Physical Injury

This category includes physical injuries, often associated with pain. The word for fracture is *gau*, but this also may be applied to muscle, ligament, and tendon strains. When used as an adjective, the word also applies to ailments of a serious nature such as *failele gau* (see ailments of women) and *fulū gau* (severe flu). More specifically, *lima gau* or *gau o le lima* refers to a broken arm or hand, and *vae gau* refers to a broken leg. The word *gau a'ano*, literally "broken flesh," refers to an internal injury, something like a bruise that may or may not be visible and lasts for a while. It, perhaps, corresponds to the Tongan ailment known as *kafo*. A bruise is known as *uno'o*. The most commonly used plants for treating these ailments are **moli 'aina** and **aloalo tai**.

The general word for pain is *tīgā*, which is often preceded or followed by a noun to indicate what part of the body hurts. The most common of these are *tua tīgā* (backache), *manava tīgā* (stomachache, noted earlier), *moa tīgā* (abdominal pain), *nifo tīgā* (toothache), and *ulu tīgā* (headache). *Tīgā tutui* refers to a severe pain. Other related terms are *fifi pa'ū* (a hernia or injury to the testes or scrotum), *sulufa* (a herniated disc in the back), and *fulu migi* (muscle fatigue). The most commonly used painkiller is probably an infusion of the grated root of kava (**'ava**), and nowadays, "Aspro" and "Panadol."

## 7. Foreign (Pālagi) Ailments

These ailments are believed to have been introduced to Samoa during the European Era (i.e., since 1830). They can often be recognized by their names, which are often a translation or transliteration of their English names. Examples of this include *fiva* (fever), *fiva samasama* (literally, "yellow fever"; however, this disease does not occur in Samoa, and the term refers instead to jaundice with fever, or hepatitis), *fiva ta'ai* (a fever that is "trapped" in the body), *kanesa* (cancer), *ma'i suka* (diabetes, literally, "sugar sickness"), and *toto maualuga* (high blood pressure). These ailments are commonly treated at the hospital, but some Samoan healers have remedies for these, even though they are *Pālagi* ailments.

### Supernaturally-Induced Ailments

As was discussed earlier, in former times most internal ailments were apparently believed to be caused by the actions of ghosts or spirits called *aitu*, usually in retribution for some action of the sufferer or some other member of his family that was offensive to these supernatural beings. Consequently, much or most of the treatment was psychological and was directed at the *aitu*. With the spread of Christianity, many of these ailments were perceived anew as natural and could thus be treated with natural means (i.e., with herbal medicines), but many of them, especially the two kinds discussed below, are still treated largely through psychological means. The category can perhaps be divided into two general types, *ma'i aitu* and *sāua*.

# 1. Possession (*Ma'i Aitu*)

*Ma'i aitu* (sometimes called *fasia*) is the most spectacular kind of supernaturally induced ailment and has often been discussed in the literature. It is best defined as a "possession" brought about by what is perceived of as a ghost or spirit, whose wrath has been raised by some action of the individual or member of his family that is irreverent or which leads to disharmony. The *aitu* literally takes over the actions of the victim. The *aitu* is thought to enter the body through the armpits, according to Goodman (1971).

It is similar in some ways to a condition called *musu*, in which the affected person becomes sullen and uncommunicative, usually because he or she has been mistreated. *Musu* also commonly means "to refuse to do or shun something," but when carried to an extreme, it can be a serious problem. Such serious cases of *musu* usually occur in young people in response to the actions of those in power, e.g., parents, *matai*, or older siblings. Since it is typically not permissible in Samoan culture for young people to verbally protest, partly because punishment is a risk, they may feel they have no recourse but to withdraw mentally, if not physically, from those causing the distress. However, *musu* is self-induced, while *ma'i aitu* is believed to be possession by a supernatural being. *Musu* may be treated by the intercession of healers, who act as social workers to try to restore harmony to the family.

One possible explanation for this type of possession behavior is hallucinations brought on by guilt. Some psychologists interpret the possession as an internalized rebellion by someone with low social status. This is supported by the fact that most people affected by *ma'i aitu* are young women; the *aitu* is often a deceased female member of the family, typically a grandmother or mother. Being possessed by an *aitu* can be an effective means of expressing feelings that would otherwise not be proper. The *aitu* may express the problem openly with little threat of retribution to the one possessed. In this state, the possessed person may say anything, even thoughts that would be a major breach of etiquette under normal circumstances. However, because it is believed that the voice speaking is that of an *aitu* and not the victim himself or herself, it is acceptable.

In *ma'i aitu*, the *aitu* is usually an ancestral or deceased member of the family, but this is not always the case. It is often one of several well-known ghosts who travel all around Samoa, and even overseas. One healer on Savai'i interviewed by the author noted that some *aitu* wanted to use his house as a resting place in their journeys around the island, but he chased them out when he believed their presence was causing illness in his family.

*Aitu* are thought particularly likely to be present at major events in Samoa, such as the annual meeting of the Congregational Christian Church of Samoa (C.C.C.S.) or at Independence Day in Apia. The two best known ghosts, both of whom are women, are Telesā and Sauma'iafe. Telesā is from the village of Lepea, and Sauma'iafe is from Sale'imoa, both on 'Upolu. They are particularly fond of bedeviling and even deceiving men into thinking they are living persons. Telesā is also believed to be jealous of women who are excessively vain, especially those with ginger-brown (*enaena*) hair. Another well-known ghost, known as Tuiatua, is from the village of Futiga in American

29

Samoa. Ghosts from other island groups in Polynesia are thought to be active in Samoa, such as Tuifiti, who is Fijian.

The *aitu* often speaks through the possessed person, usually in a voice that is different from that of the victim, to complain about how the victim is being mistreated, or about some actions by members of the village that are offensive to *aitu*. The possessed person may have phenomenal strength and, even if he or she is small, physical restraint may be difficult even for several strong men. If the *aitu* identifies itself, then the task of the healer is made easier, more so if the grievances are told. Treatment may involve the use of certain plants thought to be effective against *aitu*, or may involve just prayer. The possession is often followed by a long deep sleep, after which the victim wakes up and apparently can remember nothing of the events that have transpired.

## 2. Hard-to-Cure Ailments (*Sāua*)

The second general type of supernaturally induced ailment is called *sāua*, in which the ghost causes some physical ailment or retards the healing of already existing ailments. One variation of this is called *fa'afaiāvaina*, which is the action of the *aitu* of a recently deceased person, usually the husband, against the surviving spouse. A more correct term for supernaturally induced ailments initiated by the deceased wife against her husband is *fa'atausia*. The healer may determine that the ailment of the widow or widower is caused by the malevolent actions of the deceased, and successful treatment for this validates the diagnosis. One type is known as *tulitā fa'afaiavāina* or *tulitā sāua*, which is characterized by urinary tract problems, e.g., difficulty in urination.

Some other supernaturally induced ailments do not seem to fit well into either category, but probably are closer to the second. One is *mo'omo'o*, which is a type of headache that occurs on one side of the head. In ancient days the well-known treatment for this ailment was a chant by the *taulāitu*, accompanied by the brandishing of a spear in the direction of the patient (and the *aitu* inside him causing the headache), as noted earlier. Another type of incantation is used in one kind of treatment for *i'atolo*: the condition (and the ghost causing it) is first threatened with a stick of bamboo, with which it will be cut; then by kindling, with which it will be burned; and finally by the plant called **lau i'atolo**, with which it will be treated.

A well known type of abscess, called *'oloā* and typically found on the lower leg, is probably best classified as a type of *sāua*, although this may not be how a healer would view it. It is caused by an *aitu* called Nifoloa, who has an affinity with the people of the village of Falelima, Savai'i. He is believed to afflict people who have offended a resident of the village. He does this by biting the person and leaving the tooth (*nifo*) in the flesh, which manifests itself as an abscess. Certain medicines are believed to be effective in treating *'oloā*. When the treatment works, the tooth is extracted from the wound and is burned in a fire so that it will not return to afflict other members of the family. It is believed to explode with an audible sound when it is destroyed. Some healers equate *'oloā* with cancer, but this seems to be incorrect. The most commonly used plant for the treatment of *'oloā* is **matalafi**, which is thought to be effective in treating ailments with supernatural origins.

# TRADITIONAL SAMOAN HEALERS

The general term for a traditional healer is *fofō*, but this also refers to the practice of medicine, to the art of massage, and to those who practice massage (whether or not they use herbal medicines as well). A less used, but more polite, honorific term for a healer is *taulāsea*. If the healer specializes in, or is known for, the treatment of ghost sicknesses (*ma'i aitu*), the term *taulāitu* is sometimes used, but this is used mostly somewhat humorously. Among the *taulāsea* there is a great variation in the range of ailments treated. Some treat a wide variety of ailments with remedies they have inherited, while other treat only one or a few types of ailments.

Two specialized types of *fofō* are distinguished, *fa'atōsaga* and *fōgau*. *Fa'atōsaga*, who are almost invariably women, are usually equated with midwives, but they also perform massage for treating infertility. Normal fertility is believed to require the proper placement of the fallopian tubes in relation to the ovary; if one or the other is out of place, the abdomen is massaged in order to return them to their normal functioning position. *Fōgau* (plural *fofōgau*) are bone setters and healers of breaks and sprains. They are predominantly men, possibly because the massage and manipulation may require more strength, or because most such injuries are more familiar to men, who often receive them playing rugby or doing heavy work.

Samoan healers are not a distinct class in Samoan society, as are ministers (*faife'au*) or chiefs (*matai*); they are not elected to their position and have no formal status in the village hierarchy as a *matai* or pastor does. They are not considered to be members of a professional class, like carpenters or tattooers, since they do not receive direct payment for their services, although gifts from grateful patients can be a major source of monetary or non-monetary income.

When they are not practicing their skills, Samoan healers are no different than their patients or anyone else in the village. Often they are honored members of the society, such as the wife of a *matai*, but this is not requirement. Although they do not receive money directly for their services, and there is no formal recognition of their role in the village, they do achieve prestige by virtue of their healing skills. It is believed that God has chosen them as being worthy of his gift of healing skills. While most healers fit this profile, a few *do* look at healing as a lucrative profession, although most of them (with a few notable exceptions) still try to make a profit as subtly as possible.

The ambivalent position of healers in Samoan culture is partly because there is not always a clear boundary between healers and lay-people, due to the indistinct line between folk healing and the work of the *fofō*, noted earlier. Also contributing to the ambivalence is the fact that people may be called healers if they have just one remedy, or if they have a hundred.

It is difficult to make generalizations about healers since their practices are so varied. They belong to no organized bodies and generally do not share information among themselves, especially since it is commonly believed that their powers are a gift from God, passed on to them by their mentors because they were considered worthy. Most work alone or with an apprentice or two, but occasionally two independently trained healers may work as a pair, although they do not share their remedies.

The majority of healers are middle-aged to elderly women, possibly because much of the healing involves newborn infants and young children, who are closer to, and more often in the care of, women. In the study that led to this book, 88% of the healers interviewed were women. In other studies, Uhe (1974) recorded 68%, as did Macpherson and Macpherson (1990), but Schoeffel-Melaisa (1978) recorded 85%. When the ailment involves the genitals, the patients will usually deal with a healer of the same sex, partly out of shyness but also because of sexual taboos that would make discussion of the topic with a healer of the opposite sex difficult without making euphemistic references and using special polite names.

Healers originally learn their healing art or talent (*tāleni*) from an older person, and serve as apprenticeship for a number of years until their mentor retires or decides that the apprentice is sufficiently qualified. Training as a healer may begin at any age, but many become actively interested during their teen years. On the average, healers start their practice in their 30s, but some may begin in their early 20s.

The process of selecting someone to pass the healing art on to is very informal. Apprentices are selected on the basis of good character (such as altruism, compassion, or religious commitment), ability to learn plants and remedies, and interest in being a healer. In the vast majority of cases the apprentice is from the family of the healer, typically a child or grandchild of the healer, particularly one who cares for the healer in his or her later years. This is partly due to the belief that the family "owns" the medicines. Occasionally it is a more distant relative, but an adopted child (*tamafai*) is perfectly eligible. Only seldom are unrelated apprentices selected, and in most cases this is done only if the healer's children are not interested in becoming healers, or if the healer is childless. Most healers train at least one person, and consequently it does not appear that the profession is dying out from lack of recruits. However, many of the remedies are being lost because the plants they utilize are becoming increasingly hard to find due to the destruction of the native forests in Samoa.

The apprentices are sent out to collect medicinal plants around the house at a very early age. This typically involves much trial and error until the correct plants are learned. The apprentices are, over a long period of time, allowed to observe the treatments being given, and are given in-depth explanations of the diagnosis and treatment. Eventually, when they learn the proper herbs and techniques, they may practice some of the remedies under the direction of the healer.

Prior to practicing on his or her own, the apprentice must be spiritually prepared. Faith in God is an intricate part of the healing art, and it is believed that the healers are empowered with their *tāleni* by the grace of God, and the healing is under His divine guidance. Without this grace, their medicines would be useless. When the healer decides the apprentice is ready, the healing power is passed on to the apprentice in a ceremony called *fafano*. This typically occurs while the healer and apprentice hold hands; the healer then says a prayer, asking God to transfer the power of healing. Variation exists: sometimes the hands are held together in a bowl of water, and sometimes there is no hand-holding, only a prayer. Permission to use the remedies may be conferred singly over time or all at once. After the *fafano*, the healer may continue to heal, or may effectively retire and leave the healing to the apprentice(s) who have been trained.

Sometimes there is no *fafano* because the healer dies before it can be done. In this case, the apprentice may pray to God and receive the *tāleni* to heal directly from Him.

# HERBAL MEDICINE TODAY

## Selection of a Healer

When one becomes sick, the initial decision to be made concerns the nature of the illness—whether it is one that has *Pālagi* origins and should hence be treated by Western-trained doctors at the hospital or clinic, or one that is local in origin and should be treated by a Samoan healer. The determination of whether the ailment is *ma'i Pālagi* or *ma'i Sāmoa* is sometimes ambiguous, but usually the distinction is clear. Sicknesses such as *fulū* (flu), *māmāpala* (tuberculosis), and measles (*mīsela*) are clearly of *Pālagi* origin, while stomatitis (*pala*), boils (*ma'i sua*), and stomachache (*manava tiga*) were in Samoa long before the first Westerners and are in the province of *ma'i Sāmoa*.

Many Samoans, particularly the most educated or westernized, would pick only the first option since they do not believe in the curative powers of Samoan healers, but for most of the population, at some time in their lives, the option made by or for themis to see a Samoan healer. Serious accidents or physical injury will usually be treated at the hospital first, but the after-effects may later be treated with Samoan medicine.

Many Samoans fear going to the hospital. They will probably have to deal with a doctor or nurse that they do not know, and be placed in surroundings that are uncomfortable and unfamiliar. The treatment may be foreign and impersonal to them, unlike what they have seen in their own village while growing up, where the healer does not work for money and has plenty of time to treat the patient. They may have strong misgivings about going to a hospital for treatment of an ailment that seems to be *ma'i Sāmoa*. If they have to stay at the hospital, they will be removed from familiar surroundings and be isolated in a room or ward with visitation rules. The closer the sufferer is to Apia, with its large hospital, the more likely the choice will be for Western medicine, but this is probably due more to the fact that higher educated and more westernized Samoans usually live closer to town.

If Samoan medicine is chosen, the first healers sought are usually within the sick person's family and/or village, because the ailment can be a highly personal matter that is best kept in the family, as the cause of the ailment could lead to an "airing of dirty linen." In addition, the patient would probably feel more comfortable with a fellow family member or villager with whom they have had a prior social relationship. It is also easier to ask a healer within the family because there is no threat of refusal, and the gifts given to members of the same family need not be as large. Either the patient a family member goes to the healer to ask if he or she will take the case.

If there is no healer in the family or village, or none who feels qualified to treat the ailment, then one from another village is sought, preferably one who is known by a family member of the patient, so that at least a friendship link is present and the healer is not a stranger to the family. In this case, a family member may make the first contact to see if the healer is available and willing to take on the case.

The patient usually visits the healer, unless the illness has made it difficult or impossible to travel, in which case the healer is asked to make a house call. If the healer lives far away, then it is incumbent upon the patient's family to make generous accommodation for the healer during the duration of treatment; however, in the vast majority of cases the visits by the patient or by the healer are of short duration, and accommodation for the healer is not needed.

Samoans expect rapid and effective treatment from their healers, be they Samoan or Western-trained doctors. Lack of progress in healing will soon lead to a family decision that the treatment will not be effective in this case, or to the healer determining that the ailment cannot be treated by his or her medicines. Consequently, the patient discontinues treatment, or the healer admits defeat and suggests that they seek treatment from another healer who might have just the right remedy. Sometimes another healer will be recommended, if the first healer knows of his or her reputation with similar complaints. Sometimes the patient will be sent, or will go on their own, to the hospital to seek *Pālagi* treatment. Sometimes both methods are sought and received concurrently.

## Diagnosis

When illness or pain is perceived, the afflicted person will usually have some idea of the cause. It may be obvious, such as stomach pains from eating tainted food, back pain from lifting a heavy object, or bleeding from a knife cut. This will usually lead to some type of self-treatment—induced vomiting, bed rest, or application of sap or leaf juice in the above cases. There are several well known remedies, generally called folk medicines, for treating these easily recognized and treated ailments. If the diagnosis is

Fig. 7. A healer diagnoses a child's ailment.

not obvious and/or the self-treatment is ineffective, the person will see a healer. Medicines used by the healers are their own combinations or treatments, and are proprietary (owned) medicines.

The first step of diagnosis involves a discussion of the symptoms of the illness (Fig. 7). If the illness is of uncertain origin, such as abdominal pains or an ailment that goes on for a long time without abating, then the healer may question the patient to determine if there is some social cause (i.e., whether there is some interpersonal dispute that is causing the ailment or hindering the cure). Sometimes the patient will be asked personal questions that relate to interpersonal relationships in the family.

If the healer is unable to satisfactorily diagnose the ailment (i.e., the healer believes that he or she does not have a cure for what appears to be the ailment), he or she may politely refuse to take the case and refer the patient to another healer or to the hospital. Outright refusal in Samoan medicine is not a normal occurrence, however, even if there are strained relations between the healer and patient, because the healing powers are believed to be given by God, and it is not a mortal's place to pass judgment. Misuse of curative powers might lead to their loss in such cases. However, some healers will politely refuse treatment on days they consider their days off, typically Saturday or Sunday.

If, based on the preliminary diagnosis, the healer believes that he or she has the appropriate treatment, the case will be taken. The healer will first give the patient the diagnosis. Samoan healers do not try to hide any aspects of their healing. They do not even conceal the ingredients of their remedies, since they believe that even though someone else may make up the medicine in the same way, the cure would be ineffective since they do not own the remedy and do not have the requisite *tāleni*. They may give permission to others to prepare the medicine for a certain case, particularly if the patient lives a long distance from the healer, but this permission is usually given on a temporary basis and for the specific case at hand. Sometimes they may even give the remedy as a *meaalofa* (gift) on a permanent basis. However, the healers usually prefer to keep the remedies for themselves and their family, since only then can they vouch for the efficacy of the cure.

If the healer believes that the ailment has a social cause, then he or she will try to identify the source, i.e., which relationships are strained between the patient and friends, fellow villagers, or family. Samoans generally believe that God (or faith in God) can cure ailments but that He does not cause them. Thus, social ailments are due either to stress and anxiety in the sufferer or to the actions of *aitu* in retribution for some sins of the family. The healer's goals are to identify the disharmony causing the ill health, and to find solutions to the problem, i.e., reduce the stress or friction. The job is made easier if the healer is from the same family or village, and may already know of certain strained relationships. If the source is an *aitu*, that spirit will also have to be placated or dealt with.

Supernatural agency is implicated if what appears to be a simple physical problem does not respond to normal treatment, or if the ailment is an obvious "possession." In such cases, a healer, sometimes known as a *taulāitu*, who treats such ailments, is consulted. If the source of the ailment is not readily apparent, then the healer may look into disharmony between other members of the family or village. This kind of delving

35

into interpersonal relationships is a delicate process, since it may lead to much strife, bringing up latent or more openly disharmonious relationships.

There is another type of diagnosis that should be mentioned here—one using supernatural means. The most typical form of this is called *fai pelē*, card playing (Fig. 8). In this method, the physic/healer (or dealer!) lays out a series of cards, and from the arrangement that appears is either able to determine the source of the ailment or who the patient should go to for treatment. Most traditional healers are skeptical of this practice, but superstitious or desperate people who have not found a cure for their ailments may resort to them. There are not very many *fai pelē* in Samoa, but they are also known to occur in Tonga, the Cook Islands, and elsewhere. Playing cards are a Western introduction, and the origin of their use in diagnostis in Polynesia is not clear.

The same process is often used by these *fai pelē* to help locate lost or stolen items. Other methods of diagnosis, such as looking into a bowl of water, are used by some psychics, but these are varied and uncommon.

It may be accurate to say that the real diagnosis occurs after a sickness has been healed. The cause of the ailment may be judged to be the one that was last treated—the one that is specific for the last-used medicine. However, the body has a way of healing itself, and also, an earlier-used, slow-acting medicine might have actually been the one responsible for the cure. If the patient is seeing a Samoan healer and a doctor at the hospital at the same time, then the real cause may be obscured.

Fig. 8. Psychics who use cards (*fai pelē*) sometimes diagnose ailments.

### Treatment

Although the system of traditional healers is largely an individualized one, with no written rules, the rights and obligations between healer and patient are generally understood in the cultural context. However, since there is much variation in treatment, misunderstandings sometimes result.

Once the healer and the patient agree to begin treatment, the process involves counseling, massage, use of herbal medicines, or a combination of these. The consultation itself may have curative powers if the problem was a social one that the healer helps resolve by advising the patient and family on what is wrong. Just listening to the patient may be helpful, since the personal one-on-one contact validates the patient's importance to the society. Matters can be discussed that would otherwise remain hidden. A strong case can also be made for the beneficial effects of the patient's belief in the curative powers of the healer—a "placebo effect."

Treatment may be daily, twice daily (as in the case of massage for broken bones and strains), or less frequently. Twice daily treatments usually occur in the morning and evening. Several visits are usually needed for treatment, either at regular intervals or when certain symptoms appear or fail to appear. Treatment continues until the patient is healed, the patient dies, or when either the healer or the patient do not think the treatment is working or will work. If the healer believes the treatment is ineffective, he or she will usually refer the patient to another healer or to the hospital. The patient may withdraw at any time with little formality or obligation, and will look for another healer with or without the recommendations of the current healer. However, this is not usually done without the concurrence of the current healer so as not to offend them, or to jeopardize further attempts with other healers.

Successful treatment sometimes ends with a formal ceremony known as *fa'atā'ele* (bathing), but there is much variation in this and in many cases it is quite informal. Most healers probably do not use any formal closing ceremony, and those that do may use it only when the treatment was for a supernaturally induced ailment (*sāua*), since it is believed the treatment helps to prevent recurrence of the ailment, or to rid the body of residues of the medicine. The plants typically used in the bath are species that are believed to be repugnant to spirits.

The bath may be in the form of a sponge bath (Fig. 9), a bath in a pool, or as a *fa'apūlou* (literally, "a covering"). In the latter process, the patient is placed under a kind of tent made of sheets, mats, or tapa cloth (*siapo*) in which is a bowl of steaming medicine is placed for the patient to inhale (Fig. 10). The latter is used particularly, but not always, after treatment involving internal medicines. Some healers who do not use a closing treatment believe that others may use it as a means of receiving a greater reward from the patient.

Successful treatment may produce much gratitude, and in the case of women treated for infertility, the new mother may even name her child after the healer. Unsuccessful treatment does not necessarily reflect badly on Samoan medicine; the ailment could have been too difficult to heal, or perhaps the right healer was not consulted.

Samoan healers also practice outside of Samoa, in much the same way as they do in Samoa. There are many healers operating in Hawai'i, the U.S. West Coast, New Zealand, and wherever else there are large resident populations of Samoans. The practice is basically the same, except for the absence of many of the plants needed to prepare the medicines. However, if a certain Samoan plant is needed, the healer will arrange for someone in Samoa to obtain the required plant, which is then carried by someone traveling to the country. It may be transported frozen or fresh, although there can be problems with fresh material at the airport agriculture inspection (if it is declared, but it often isn't).

Unlike in the past, surgery is rarely practiced nowadays, other than, perhaps, for the lancing of boils. Even the usual circumcision of young boys is now done in the hospital, typically in groups of young boys when they become five years old (Kinloch

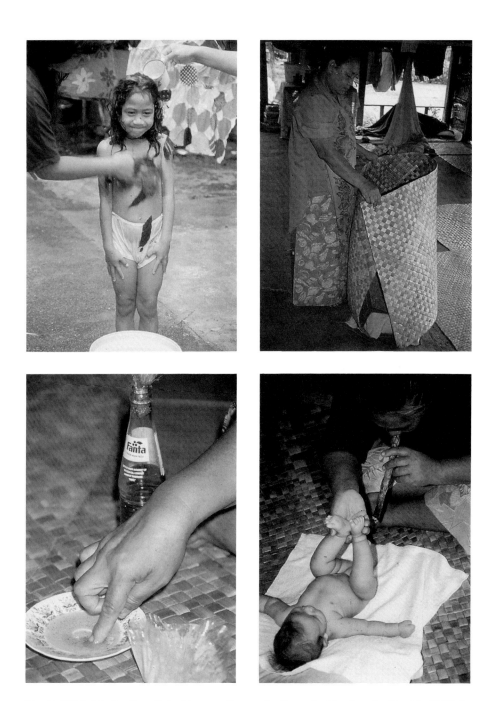

Fig. 9. (T,L) A bath of medicinal leaves often marks the end of treatment. Fig. 10. (T,R) A patient is sometimes given a steambath under mats and/or blankets. Fig. 11. (B,L) *Lega* from the turmeric plant is mixed with coconut oil. Fig. 12. (B,R) Smoke blown from a hollow, burning breadfruit twig is used in a treatment for *ila*.

38

1985a). The current practice of circumcision (called *peritome*, from the Greek words "to cut around") is a variation of a traditional Polynesian practice (which is technically a "superincision").

## Giving of Gifts

The treatment of sickness by the healer is considered to be an act of love, in which the healing powers given by God are employed. Consequently, it is not considered to be a profession in which the patient pays for the treatment, as in countries lacking socialized medicine. A healer who requested or obviously expected payment would, it is believed, lose the healing power and would be in breech of Samoan social values.

However, the explanation is not all that simple. While payment is not given, gifts customarily are. The giving of gifts (*meaalofa*) is an integral part of Samoan culture, and for someone to receive a favor from another—in this case a major favor involving time and effort on the part of the healer—without reciprocating in some way, would be considered selfish by most Samoans. Consequently, small gifts are usually given before, during, and/or after treatment. The nature and size of the gift is entirely at the discretion of the patient's family. Sometimes it is small amounts of money, sometimes food, and other times fine mats (especially at the end of a successful treatment). Gifts typically given during treatment are small amounts of money (in Western Samoa, less than a *tala*—about 40 cents U.S.), and these are discreetly presented so as not to appear as a payment, which would risk refusal. Gifts to healers of the same family as the patient are, because of family ties, likely to be smaller.

At the end of treatment, in a ceremony called a *fa'amāvaega o le fofō* (literally, "saying good bye to the healer"), a more formal and larger gift may be presented by the patient's family out of gratitude to the healer. The healer will typically make little fanfare of the gift, unless he or she feels it is too generous, in which case the healer may politely request that the family should take some of it back. Other payments may be made in the form of donations when the healer has a *fa'alavelave* (a major social event requiring the collection of large amounts of goods and food, such as a wedding, birth, or death), or when donations can be given in the name of the healer for someone else's *fa'alavelave*.

## Preparing the Medicine

Samoan herbal medicine is almost always prepared with plant material, usually collected fresh. The only major exceptions are the use of coconut oil (*suāu'u*), turmeric powder (*lega*), coconut oil, ashes, and smoke. There is only occasional use of other things, such as sea cucumbers (*sea*), raw fish, or breast milk. Also, "holy water" that has been blessed by a priest is sometimes used in healing, at least by a few Catholic healers.

Coconut oil is made from coconut cream that has been squeezed out of grated copra. The cream, often mixed with fragrant flowers or bark, is allowed to sit in the sun until the clear oil comes to the surface. This oil, also called Samoan oil, is then collected and bottled, and can commonly be found for sale in the open market in Apia. In American

Fig. 13. (T,L) Medicinal fern rhizomes are collected from a large tree. Fig. 14 (T,R) A spoon is used to scrape bark from a tree trunk. Fig. 15. (B,L) Root bark is scraped off into a dish. Fig. 16. (B,R) Chopped medicinal leaves stored in a *fuʻafuʻa* (*Kleinhovia hospita*) leaf.

Samoa, Samoan oil is not as readily made or available, and commercial "baby oil" is often used in its place, since Samoan oil itself apparently has no healing qualities.

*Lega* is the yellow turmeric powder prepared from the rhizome of the **ago** plant in a time-consuming process, but most of the *lega* used, at least in the Apia area, is bought in the open market in small plastic bags. The *lega* is mixed with coconut oil before being applied to the skin (Fig. 11). The only significant use of ashes is in the treatment of burns. The green or dried leaves of **'ofe Sāmoa**, Polynesian bamboo, are burned, and the ashes then mixed with coconut oil.

The most significant use of smoke is for the treatment of *ila*. This practice, which has also been reported from Niue, Tonga, and in the Samoan community in New Zealand, is employed by relatively few healers, since herbal preparations are believed to have the same healing effects. In the process, the healer lights one end of a hollow twig of **'ulu** (breadfruit) and blows the smoke through it onto the baby's buttocks (Fig. 12). Another component of some medicines is aspirin (Aspro) or other pain killers (such as Panadol), an interesting addition from the Western pharmacopoeia.

Plants are usually gathered by the healer (Fig. 13) or by his or her apprentices because they are best qualified to know what is needed. Healers who are old and infirm will often rely on their apprentices or other members of the family. Because of the loss of native lowland forests, some plants formerly used in remedies are no longer employed, and although remedies using these hard-to-find plants are still known by the healer, they are seldom used. Sometimes, however, a relative of the sick person may live near the source of a hard-to-find plant (usually on Savai'i) and is asked to collect and send it to 'Upolu (or overseas, as noted above).

Most of the plants utilized by the healers are gathered from around their houses (either as weeds or plants that are purposefully cultivated) or can readily be obtained in the village or adjacent plantations. Other than *lega* noted above, medicinal plants are rarely if ever obtained in the open market, unless the plant is being sold for other reasons (e.g., for food).

Few rules govern the collection of plant material. Plants may be collected at any time of the day by anyone. However, the plant material must be healthy. One interesting exception to the absence of collecting rules is the harvesting of a coconut used in treating *la'ofia*, the fetus swallowing the meconium in the amniotic fluid before birth. In this case, the coconut is cut from the tree and carried down rather than being dropped. The husk is then crushed and the juice given to the infant.

Another interesting practice is the collection of matching pairs (*faisoa*) used in many medicines. The reasons for this are unclear, but may be based on ancient superstition. The same practice is reported from Tonga. However, in the Cook Islands and Tahiti, many medicines call for the use of leaves in multiples of three, and in Hawai'i multiples of four is a common occurrence. There is much variation in this in Samoa, with some healers restricting pairing to certain plants and others using it for all plants. When only certain plants are used in pairs, these are usually plants, most commonly **matalafi** and **fue sina**, that are thought to be repellent to spirits.

The plant material is believed to lose its strength if preparation is delayed too long, which accounts for the use of fresh rather than dried material, and under normal circumstances few plants are used more than a day after their collection. However, nowadays plastic bags and refrigerators are used to prolong the viability of the plant material and its active chemicals, which is especially important if the plants are to be shipped to another island or overseas.

The most commonly used plant parts are the leaves (*lau*) and bark (*pa'u lā'au* or *'ōgālā'au*). Leaves are typically pinched or cut off with a knife rather than torn off. Mature leaves are usually used, but some remedies call for leaf buds or immature leaves (*moemoe*), or, less commonly, the terminal bud of the plant (*mu'amu'a*). Some remedies call for a specific part of the leaf, e.g., the petiole of a breadfruit leaf (**'ulu**) for treating eye ailments (*mata pa'ia*).

Tree trunks are scraped with anything handy that works, most commonly a kitchen knife, a spoon (Fig. 14), or (in former times) a shell. Some remedies specifically call for the bark from a branch (*lālā*). The outer bark is first removed, and the inner bark collected. Roots (*a'a*), either aerial (as in the case of **aoa** and **fasa**) or underground, are sometimes used. Underground roots, such as breadfruit (**'ulu**), are dug up, washed, the outer layer scraped off, and the inner layer collected (Fig. 15). Rhizomes (*i'o*) are also used, especially from plants such as ginger (**fiu**), wild ginger (**'avapui**), and the fern **lau 'auta** (also called **lau magamaga**). However, the distinction between *i'o* and *a'a* is not always clear, and the names are sometimes used interchangeably.

Less commonly, the sap (*'āpulupulu*), fruits (*fua or fuā lā'au*, or if immature, *fua moto*), flowers (*fugā lā'au*, or less specifically, *fuā lā'au*), and seeds (*fatu*) are used. There is some confusion when outsiders record information on usage of flowers and fruits, since they are both typically called *fua*. The most frequently used plant saps come from **aloe** and **lā'au fai lafa**, both of which are recent introductions to Samoa, the former used to treat cuts and burns, the latter for ringworm. Vapor from a broken leaf of **nonu** is used in treating a sty (*matafā*), which is further explained on p. 47.

The most commonly used flower is that of **nonu** as part of the remedy for treating a sty just mentioned above. Some healers recognize the existence of separate male and female plants. However, these do not necessarily correspond to male and female plants (based on flower parts) recognized by botanists, but are based more on the size or shape of the flower, leaves (as in **nonu** and **matalafi**), or the whole plant (as in **aoa**). A plant considered male is called *tane* (male) and one considered female, *fafine*. The most commonly used seed is that of **lama** (candlenut), which is chewed or crushed and used to treat skin ailments. There is also at least one lichen (*Ramalina* sp.?) that is used in the treatment of warts (*lafitoga*) and yaws (*tona*).

The leaves and bark or rhizome scrapings are collected in a receptacle, such as a leaf (e.g., **fa'i, nonu**, or **fu'afu'a**), cup, or plastic bag and carried to the preparation site. A leaf receptacle (Fig. 16) is usually folded into a pouch and tied shut with a string, piece of fiber, or the petiole.

Leaves used in medicines are cut up (*tipi*) or crushed (*tu'itu'i*) on a wooden cutting board (Fig. 17) like one used for preparing food (but not the same one), a mortar made of a flattened rock, or the shell of a giant clam (Fig. 18). Because of its small size, the clam shell (*atigi faisua*) can only be used for relatively small amounts of medicine. The cutting is done with an ordinary knife used for other kitchen chores. The pestle (Fig. 19) is usually a smooth, round to oblong, weathered basalt rock found in streams or estuaries. A metal cocoa pounder called a *ma'a tu'i koko* is sometimes used instead.

42

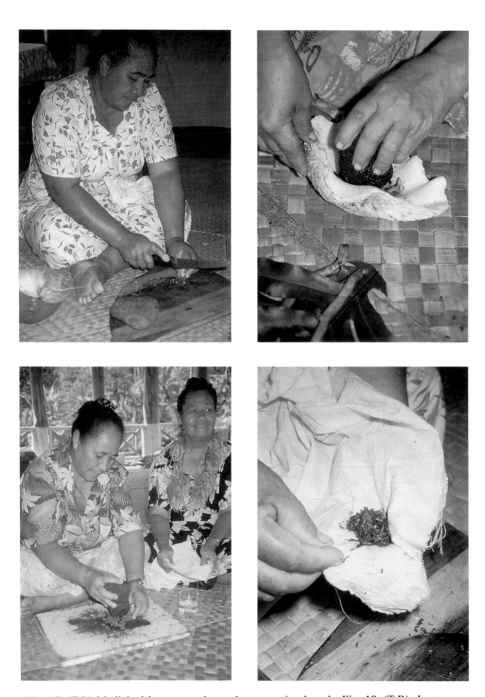

Fig. 17. (T,L) Medicinal leaves are chopped on a cutting board. Fig. 18. (T,R) Leaves are sometimes crushed in a giant clam shell. Fig. 19. (B,L)  A stone is typically used to crush medicinal plants. Fig. 20. (B,R) Chopped leaves are put into a piece of gauze.

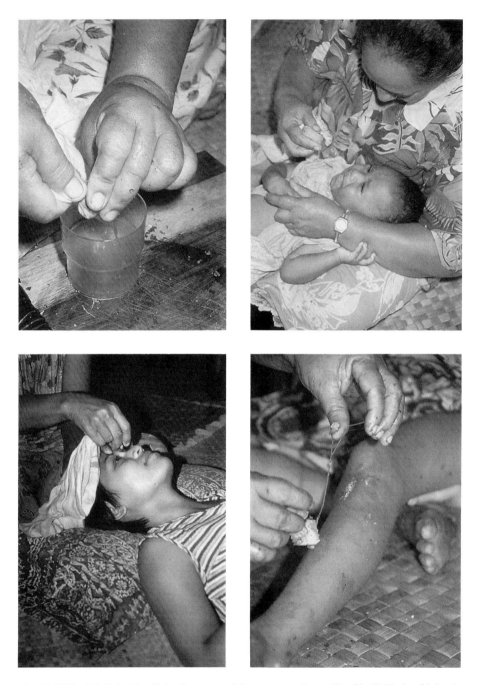

Fig. 21 (T,L)  Medicinal leaf juice is squeezed from a gauze bag.  Fig. 22. (T,R)  Leaf juice is dripped into the mouth of a baby.  Fig. 23. (B,L) Leaf juice eyedrops are squeezed from a cloth bag.  Fig. 24. (B,R.) Leaf juice lotion is applied to sores on the leg.

However, nowadays most of the maceration is done simply by cutting the leaves on a board.

If the medicine is to be administered as an infusion, the crushed or scraped plant material isgathered and placed into a small piece of mesh or fabric. Originally the fabric-like material (*lau a'a*) found at the base of a coconut leaf was used for this purpose, but nowadays it is often a piece of fine cloth or gauze (*kosi*) instead (Fig. 20). The cloth is bought at a store and the gauze is obtained from a pharmacy, or local clinic or hospital. Healers recognized by the hospitals are often given the gauze for free.

The piece of gauze or cloth is fashioned into a bag, which is then dipped and squeezed into a cup or glass of water to make an infusion of the medicine (Fig. 21). The water is usually fresh, and may be taken from any clean source; it is usually at room temperature, but in some remedies is heated before being used to make the infusion. For babies who cannot or will not drink (*inu*) the infusion, the juice from the moistened bag of medicine is dripped into their mouths (Fig. 22). With some infant ailments, particularly stomatitis (*pala*), the medicinal plant material may be chewed and then dripped (*pipisi*) into the mouth of the infant. If eye drops (*tului ai mata*) are called for, the moistened bag is squeezed directly over the eyes (Fig. 23).

If the medicine is drunk, it is believed to be absorbed into the body to effect its cure. However, in cases of respiratory congestion, some medicines act as emetics to cause vomiting (*pua'i*) and force the mucus out of the mouth and throat. In cases where food poisoning is suspected, the medicine used is known to have a purgative (*vai fa'atafe*) effect.

If the leaves are to be applied directly to the skin, they are either crushed in the hands and rubbed or massaged onto the skin as a lotion (Fig. 24), applied as a poultice to be covered with a bandage or piece of cloth, or squeezed or rolled in the hands until the juice drips onto the skin, as is done with the leaves of **fue Saina** for treating bleeding wounds (see Fig. 3—6). Medicinal leaves used under poultices are replaced at the time the bandage or cloth is removed for inspection of the wound or infection. Some leaves, when used whole, are first softened over a fire (e.g., **nonu**). **Nonu** leaves are usually used in preparations where the medicines are wrapped up and roasted (*tunu*) on charcoals or are heated in a pan over a flame (Fig. 25). Infusions of medicine may be either patted (*pōpō*) or rubbed (*mili*) onto the skin.

In some cases, Samoan oil (made from coconut as noted earlier) is used as the solvent. These are usually applied externally and allow the medicine to adhere to the skin better. The plant most commonly used for this is **ago**, whose powdered rhizome extract, turmeric (*lega*), is added to the oil and applied to skin sores. Some remedies, dissolved in oil, are used as purgatives, but the oil by itself is also effective. External medicines are usually applied with the finger or with a piece of cloth, but occasionally a chicken feather (*fulu moa*) is used.

Most medicines are used immediately after preparation, but some are made to be used over a period of several days. Medicines made from grated bark are often boiled (*saka*) to sterilize them, or more frequently, the water is first boiled (*fa'apuna*) and the medicinal ingredients added afterwards. These sterilized medicines may be used for up to a week, particularly if they are also refrigerated. Boiling is typically used when the patient lives far from the healer, and daily visits are impractical.

45

Other medicines are boiled and the steam from them is utilized. In these cases, the patient puts his head under a piece of material or a sheet covering a bowl or pan of the steaming medicine and inhales in the vapor. This process is similar to the *fa'apūlou* noted earlier, and is used for the direct treatment of an ailment, often of the respiratory tract. Sometimes, however, it is used as the closing act of treatment, probably meant to rid the body of any *aitu* that may be retarding recovery, to remove the residues of the medicines used, or to formally mark the end of treatment.

Most Samoan remedies are composed of material from only a single species, but sometimes two or more species are involved. Compound medicines with more than two elements are a distinct minority, but one remedy recorded by the author included twelve species. The remedies are usually memorized by the healers, but some healers have (or had in their early healing years) a notebook with recorded remedies (Fig. 26).

Fig. 25. A fire is lit to heat medicine wrapped in **nonu** leaves.

During the preparation and administration of medicine, most healers use a silent prayer requesting that God facilitate their healing of the ailment. Prayers are also given orally during the evening service, asking that God continue to give them the power to heal. This is done regularly, whether or not the healer is currently treating a patient. The healers believe that God has given them the power or talent (*tāleni*) to use the plants, and although other unauthorized persons may try to duplicate their remedy, it is almost universally believed that the medicine will be useless or spoiled if it is not prepared by, or with the blessing of, the owner of the remedy.

In addition to God's effects on the treatment, aspects of several kinds of treatment involve supernatural elements. In one interesting treatment, for a type of children's ailment called *ila toso*, the healer places the baby on a mat (*fala lili'i pepe*) and pulls it around her in a circle (Fig. 27). This is done over several days, with one rotation on the first day, two on the second, and so on. Some healers subsequently discard the mat, others allow the mat, which is often woven by the baby's family, to be reused. It is not clear if this medical practice is related to the actions of *aitu* or is based upon some ancient superstition, but it certainly involves supernatural belief. Another unusual treatment is the burning of the hardened core (the *nifo* or "tooth") of an abscess called *'oloā* so that it will not reinfect other members of the family, as noted earlier.

A third example is the use of **nonu** in treating a sty (*matafa*). There is much minor variation in this, but typically a **nonu** leaf is first broken near the sty, presumably to disperse some vapor onto the ailment. Then a flower is moved in a circular motion around the sty, for a number and direction that may vary with different healers, before it is touched to the sty. Typically, a sty on the left eye will be treated with the right hand, and one on the right eye with the left hand.

## Samoan Massage

Massage is an ancient practice, and similar practices with the same or related names are found throughout Polynesia. It is most commonly applied to strains, sprains, or bone fractures (*gau*), body pains such as headache and backache, and treatment of *to'ala* described earlier. The general term for massage is *fofo*, and the same term is applied to specialists who practice it (with or without herbal medicine). However, for everyday aches and pains, most adolescent and adult Samoans know the basics and will frequently treat themselves or be called on to treat others. Massage usually involves the use of Samoan oil to reduce friction (Fig. 28). Headaches and sometimes other body aches are usually massaged using a ti leaf (**lau ti**) or **nonu** leaf and water (Fig. 29).

A specialist who treats fractures is called a *fogau*. These healers are usually men, as opposed to other herbal medicine practitioners, who are mostly female. The reason for the male dominance in this field is because more strength is needed for the massage and manipulation of broken limbs, or perhaps because the fracture and strain injuries more commonly affect men (especially from rugby) and are well known to them. The *fogau* sets the bones by manipulating the broken parts back into the correct position and

Fig. 26. A healer with a written record of her remedies.

angle. The injured area is then massaged and covered with wet compresses to reduce swelling. Use of the injured area is discouraged; in the case of a broken arm, the limb is sometimes immobilized by wrapping it with stiff rods (Fig. 30) split from a coconut frond stalk (*lapalapa*), which is probably an ancient practice.

Before massage begins, the *fofo* feels the injured or painful area with the fingertips. Depending the diagnosis, any one of three or four different types of massage may be

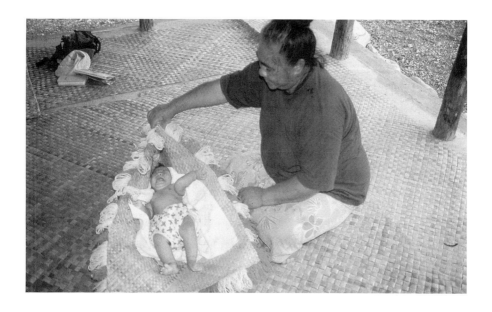

Fig. 27. A baby is pulled around (*toso*) a healer in a treatment for *ila.*

Fig. 28. A patient is massaged with baby oil as Mrs. Doubtfire looks on.

used. The most physical kind is called *tu'itu'i*, which involves a vigorous hitting of the affected area with the fist, the palms, or the sides of the open hand. This corresponds to a massage called *tukituki* in Tokelau and possibly Tonga.

Less severe is *lomilomi*, which is application of pressure or kneading with the knuckles of the fist (and rarely with the feet). The knuckles are pushed between the muscles and moved in a circular fashion. This corresponds to the massage of the same name in Tokelau and Hawai'i, to *romi* in the Cook Islands, and apparently to *tolotolo* and/or *fotofota* in Tonga.

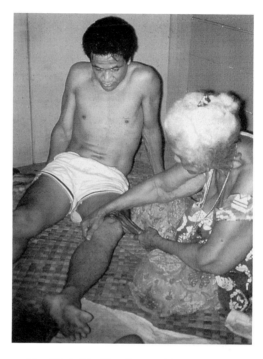

The third and gentlest kind of Samoan massage is *milimili*, which usually involves gentle pressure with the fingertips or palms, with Samoan oil applied to reduce friction. *Milimili* is probably the same as the *milimili* of Tokelau and the *amoamo* of Tonga. It is usually applied to boils, causing them to burst, and in cases where a more vigorous massage would increase the pain. A fourth kind of massage noted by Macpherson and Macpherson (1990), called *eneene* or *ene*, is described as a "light touching, almost pinching of the skin with the finger tips..."

Fig. 29. A ti leaf is often used in massage of sore muscles and headaches.

### Incantations in Healing

In former times, incantations by the priest-healers (*taulāitu*) were a part of at least some kinds of treatments, usually in the form of a challenge to the *aitu* thought to be the cause of the ailment, sometimes accompanied by a threat. The best known incantation was for treatment of *mo'omo'o* (described on p.30). Although it was first recorded over 130 years ago, variations of it are still used today to treat *mo'omo'o*, along with the use of a spear or staff (Moyle 1973a), or in one case seen by the author, a pair of knives.

Moyle also recorded current usage of incantations in treating hiccups (*to'omaunu*), a headache called *fe'e* (literally, "octopus," that effects the whole head), a stomach ailment called *osofā punimoa* characterized by blockage of food entering the stomach, a fish bone lodged in the throat (*laoa*), a swelling in the groin (*puga*), *ila*, which is, as noted earlier, a group of ailments of infants, and *sila'ilagi*, a boil on the upper body or limbs. However, incantations are infrequently used in healing today.

49

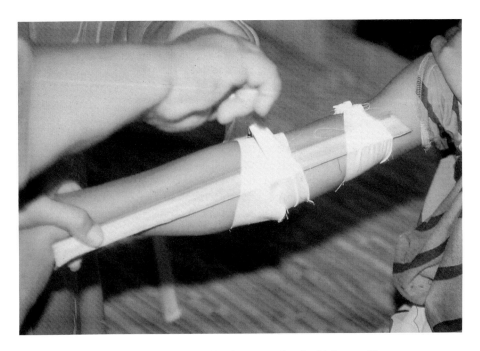

Fig. 30. Splints of split coconut frond midrib are still
occasionally used for arm injuries.

## Treatment of Possession (*Ma'i Aitu*)

Treatment for *ma'i aitu* is one of the most interesting and well-studied types of Samoan medical care. These are the ailments most likely to be treated by non-medicinal means, but detailing these mostly religious treatments is beyond the scope of this book. In the standard treatment for a person afflicted with *ma'i aitu*, a healer who has a reputation for treating the sickness is summoned. A term sometimes applied to a *fofō* who treats *ma'i aitu* is *taulāitu*, an ancient term used for the spirit doctors of the past. The term is used nowadays almost humorously, and most of the healers who treat these ailments treat other ailments as well.

It is apparent that many cases of *ma'i aitu* are faked and the healer must first determine whether a case is genuine. One way to determine if the "possession" is real or faked is to hit the patient—a true *ma'i aitu* victim will not feel the pain because he or she is totally under the control of the *aitu*, but a pretender will. In these faked cases, a whipping can sometimes effect a miraculous cure! Another method is to apply an *aitu* medicine, which is believed to be repellent to spirits, and watch the reaction of the patient.

If the healer believes the possession is real, he or she will try to ascertain who the *aitu* is and the nature of the grievance. Dealing with *aitu* is believed to be dangerous to the healer, and consequently the healer usually applies to his/her skin an infusion of a plant believed to be repellent to ghosts. Several plants are well known as being effective

50

in treating supernaturally induced ailments. These are believed to be offensive to *aitu*, and by rubbing the infusion onto the body or by dripping it into the mouth, nose, ears, and eyes, the *aitu* will be forced to depart. The plants most commonly used are **matalafi, fue sina, usi, nonu, fue manogi,** and **'ava'avaaitu.**

The best known of these (and believed to be the strongest) is **matalafi** (*Psychotria insularum*), whose medicinal usage seems to be restricted to Samoa, although it also occurs in Tonga and Niue. **Fue sina** (*Vigna marina*) is also very commonly employed but is believed to be mild in its effects, and is often used in treating children with non-possession ailments (i.e., *sāua*). **Nonu** (*Morinda citrifolia*) is commonly used in Samoa, Tonga and elsewhere for the same purposes. **Usi** (*Euodia hortensis*), a very strong-smelling plant grown around houses, is believed to repel ghosts with its overpowering odor. An element of superstition in the preparation of the medicine involves the collecting of leaves in pairs (*faisoa*), as noted earlier. Nowadays, perfumes are used by some healers to achieve the same results, especially by those living overseas who do not have access to the traditional plants.

Some healers believe that the *aitu* will try to prevent them from collecting the plants, either by stripping the leaves from the trees (typically of **matalafi**, which *aitu* seem to fear the most), or by physically impeding their efforts to reach the plants. Once the healer does reach a **matalafi** plant, he or she may then rub themselves with it so that the *aitu* can no longer interfere. The treatment is usually accompanied by a prayer. Upon completion of treatment, a closing ceremony called *fa'atā 'ele* is often given to the patient as a bath or steam bath, as discussed earlier.

Ghosts are commonly believed by healers to reside in four places in the body—in the ears, armpits, the back of the knees, and the tops of the toes. The medicinal plants are typically dripped first into the ears, causing the ghost to move to the armpits, with further treatment causing further movement.

Once the appropriate prayers are said and the healer is protected by medicinal plants, the healer will try to talk to the ghost to learn his or her identity and the reason for the possession. If this is ascertained and the ghost has vented its grievances, it may leave voluntarily and further treatment may not be necessary. However, when there is no response from the ghost (i.e., the patient is not able to communicate because of a deep sleep or the possession), the medicinal plants noted above are either dripped into the eyes, ears, nose, and mouth, and/or the infusion is given as a sponge bath. Sometimes the patient is wrapped up in old clothing or burlap sacks, based on the belief that the ghost will then be shamed into talking.

## THE FUTURE OF SAMOAN MEDICINE

Western medicine has much to learn from the study of indigenous medical systems of other parts of the world. This applies to the practices of the healers themselves, as well as to the medicinal plants used. Western medicine has tended to discredit the native medical systems it has largely replaced, but there is wisdom of centuries of experimentation in most native medical practices.

It is apparent that much of the current traditional medicinal practice is not like what it was prior to 1830, when there was much less emphasis on medicinal plants. However, by trial and error, the pharmacopoeia has developed to such a degree that even after a long competition with Western medicine it is still the system of choice for many Samoans.

While it is certain that many of the herbal medicines described in this book are effective, it is also likely that many of them are not. Also, what works in Samoan culture may not work outside of Samoa, either because of differences in pathogens and health conditions, or because of the strong personal influence of healers. Some of the cures achieved by the *fofō* are probably due to the "placebo effect," wherein patients are more likely to recover from an ailment if they *believe* the treatment will work. This faith in the treatment or in the healer is an important aspect of medicine, and makes recovery credited to herbal medicines versus that credited to the belief in the healer's powers very difficult to distinguish.

It is not likely that any miracle drugs will come out of Samoa, although recently one plant (**mamala**, *Omalanthus nutans*) has shown promise in killing the AIDS virus in a test tube (although interviews with healers has not shown any significant use of the plant in treating viral diseases in Samoa). Although Norton *et al.* (1973) and Cox *et al.* (1989) have shown pharmacological activity in many Samoan plants, neither has shown correlations to how the plants are used medicinally, nor is it easy to translate their effective use in Samoa to a pharmacological product that can benefit the rest of the world. The promise of Samoan medicinal plants in no way can compare with that of China or the ancient American cultures, where the pharmacopoeia has developed over thousands of years. Also, since many of the most valuable medicinal plants are poisonous to some degree, Samoa, with few poisonous plants, is at a disadvantage. Another disadvantage is that Samoa has a much smaller selection of plants to choose from, because of its smaller flora. However, further research is needed in this field. and hopefully the following appendix of Samoan medicinal plant uses may help to focus further study.

Because Western medicine has not proven its superiority over Samoan medicine, and because Samoa is a conservative country that values its traditions, Samoan medicine is likely to retain continued support, and will likely coexist with Western medicine for the foreseeable future. Nearly all of the healers interviewed during the author's 1994 studies were training replacements for themselves. The biggest threat seems to be the loss of native forest, which makes it very difficult to find some of the plants needed to make some medicines. This points up the need for strong conservation measures so that the medicinal plants, as well as other plant species, will not disappear. What is also needed is the establishment of botanical gardens that grow medicinal plants, particularly the rare ones.

# CHAPTER III.
## SAMOAN MEDICINAL PLANTS

This chapter comprises an enumeration and discussion of the 84 most commonly used and best known medicinal plants in Samoa, listed in alphabetical order by their Samoan names. Since many of the species have more than one Samoan name, alternate names are listed in parentheses. Each entry includes the scientific name, which generally concurs with *Flora vitiensis nova: a new flora of Fiji* (Smith 1979—1991). The italicized scientific name is followed by the names (sometimes abbreviated) of one or more botanists who named the plant. If there is a name (sometimes two) in parentheses, it is of the botanist who originally named the plant; the name following the parentheses belongs to the person (or persons) who transferred it to its currently recognized genus. However, these authors' names are mostly of interest to professional botanists and are of little concern to others. Beneath the scientific name is the "family" to which the plant belongs, and the English common name (if any).

The introductory lines are followed by a brief description of the plant, including where it originated, its current range, its distribution and frequency in Samoa, and uses other than medicinal ones. The second paragraph is a brief description of the plant, to aid in identification. The last paragraph under "**USES**" is an account of the Samoan medicinal uses of the plants, as reported from the literature (see Bibliography) and from interviews with 25 healers by the author in Western Samoa, American Samoa, and New Zealand in 1994.

Since the remedies given to the author were for his information only, none of the details of the these remedies, which varied greatly from healer to healer, have been recorded here. There are several reasons why it is not recommended that readers of this book try the remedies themselves: (1) no specific dosages are given, and some of the medicines are poisonous at high doses; (2) the healers themselves believe that they have a God-given talent to make the remedies work, and that others administering their remedies would have no effect; and (3) self-diagnosis of ailments is not always accurate. The author himself has tried only one of the internal remedies, and that plant usage is well known. However, many of the external remedies for first aid may be safe and effective, such as the use of aloe for burns, but discretion is advised.

Color photographs of many of the following plants may be found in *Polynesian Herbal Medicine* (Whistler 1992a), *Flowers of the Pacific Island Seashore* (Whistler 1992c), and *Wayside Plants of the Islands* (Whistler 1995). Similar remedies recorded from Tonga noted in many of the following entries are found in *Tongan Herbal Medicine* (Whistler 1992b). Most of the Samoan names may be found in an annotated checklist of Samoan plant names published earlier (Whistler 1984).

### A'ATASI

**SCIENTIFIC NAME:** *Rorippa sarmentosa* (DC.) Macbr.
**FAMILY:** Brassicaceae (mustard family)
**ENGLISH NAME:** Polynesian cress

*Rorippa sarmentosa* ranges from the Solomon Islands to the easternmost islands of Polynesia (Hawai'i and Easter Island), but it may have been an ancient introduction rather than a native species over much of this range. It is occasional as a weed of disturbed places, particularly around houses in villages, where it may be semi-cultivated for its medicinal properties. It only rarely occurs in native habitats, mostly in wet places. Its medicinal uses in Samoa and the rest of Polynesia probably date to ancient times. In Manu'a, the name **a'atasi** is also applied to another herbaceous plant with a taproot, *Boerhavia repens* (see **ufi**).

A'atasi is a small, slender, glabrous herb up to 60 cm in height, growing from a thick taproot (*a'atasi* = taproot). The alternately arranged, pinnately compound leaves up to 15 cm long are arranged in a basal rosette. The flowers are borne in terminal racemes up to 25 cm long, with four white petals less than 2 mm long. The fruit is a cylindrical pod 15—25 mm long, containing two rows of tiny seeds that are expelled when the pod splits open.

**USES:** This is one of the plants most commonly used for treating infants. An infusion of the crushed leaves or the whole plant is very commonly given to infants as a potion for treating childhood ailments known as *ila fale*, *ila mea*, and *ila fa'a'autama*, and occasionally for inflammation of the skin (*mūmū*). Juice from the crushed leaves is sometimes applied to boils (*sila'ilagi* and *ma'i sua*) and to infected wounds ('*oloā*) thought to be caused by the bite of a ghost known as Nifoloa. The juice is also occasionally dripped into the eyes of infants for treating eye injury (*mata pa'ia*) and pterygium (*moālili*).

## AGO
## (LEGA)

**SCIENTIFIC NAME:** *Curcuma longa* L.
**FAMILY:** Zingiberaceae (ginger family)
**ENGLISH NAME:** turmeric

*Curcuma longa* is widespread in the Old World tropics from West Africa to eastern Polynesia, but is thought to have originated in cultivation somewhere in Southeast Asia (it is not known to occur in the wild state), and from there was carried throughout the Pacific by early voyagers. Turmeric occurs mostly in plantations and around villages in Samoa, but is uncommon. It is esteemed throughout its range as a condiment (especially in Asia, where it is an essential ingredient in curry) and for the light yellow or yellow-orange dye extracted from the rhizome.

**Ago** is a glabrous, erect herb up to 1 m in height, arising from a fleshy, yellow, aromatic rhizome. The erect leaves have a finely parallel-veined, lanceolate to elliptic blade up to 40 cm long. The flowers are in a cylindrical spike 12—25 cm long on a leafless flowering stalk, and are borne in few-flowered clusters among the numerous, overlapping, green to reddish bracts. The white to yellow, tubular perianth (corolla plus calyx) is mostly 2.5—4 cm long. Flowering is infrequent, and no seeds are produced.

**USES:** One of the commonest treatments for stomatitis (*pala gutu*) and blisters on the lips (*'atiloto*) is to mix turmeric powder with coconut oil and rub the yellow medicine onto the sores. The same medicine is often applied to skin sores (*papala, po'u*) as well, a use also reported from Tonga. Less commonly, it is applied to skin inflammations (*mūmū*). An infusion of the scraped rhizome is sometimes taken as a potion for treating stomachache (*manava tīgā*), and less often for ulcers (*pala ga'au*), diarrhea (*manava tatā*), and urinary tract problems (*tulitā*).

## ALOALO
### (ALOALO FANUA, ALOALO VAO)

**SCIENTIFIC NAME:** *Premna serratifolia* L.
**FAMILY:** Verbenaceae (verbena family)
**ENGLISH NAME:** none

*Premna serratifolia*, formerly known as *Premna obtusifolia*, is distributed from tropical East Africa to the Marquesas Islands, and is native to Samoa, where it is occasional in coastal areas in open native vegetation, particularly on lava flows, and rarely inland in sunny places in the mountains at up to 500 m elevation.

**Aloalo** is a shrub or small tree up to 3 m or more in height. The simple, oppositely arranged leaves have an ovate to oblong blade up to 20 cm long. The tiny flowers are numerous in widely branching panicles. The white, sympetalous corolla is four-lobed and 2—3 mm long. The fruit is a black, globose drupe 3—9 mm in diameter, with the persistent, saucerlike calyx at the base.

**USES:** An infusion of the crushed leaves is often given as a potion to children to treat *mūmū tatau* and other types of inflammation (*mūmū*), and less commonly for fever (*fiva ta'ai* and *vevela*). Its use in treating inflammation is also reported from Tonga.

## ALOALO TAI
### (SUNI TAI, ALOALO SAMI)

**SCIENTIFIC NAME:** *Clerodendrum inerme* (L.) Gaertn.
**FAMILY:** Verbenaceae (verbena family)
**ENGLISH NAME:** none

*Clerodendrum inerme* ranges from tropical Asia to western Polynesia (Niue) and is found on most of the high islands of this region. It is occasional to common in Samoa on rocky or sandy beaches, as a shrub or sometimes almost vinelike in littoral forest. The flowers are showy, but the plant is utilized for little other than medicine. It is apparently sometimes called **suni tai**, which is applied more correctly to an unrelated species, *Phaleria disperma*, which is now rare in Samoa.

**Aloalo tai** is a spreading shrub up to 4 m or more in height. The simple, oppositely arranged leaves have an ovate to elliptic, acute-tipped blade 5—13 cm long. The flowers are borne one to several in axillary cymes. The showy white corolla has a narrow tube

2.5—3.5 cm long that is deeply divided at the top into five spreading lobes. The four stamens and single style are red and protrude from the flower. The green to brown, obovoid fruit is 1—1.5 cm long and at maturity splits into four 1-seeded nutlets.

USES: The crushed leaves are commonly applied to wounds (*lavea* or *manu'a*), sometimes after the mash has been wrapped in a **nonu** (*Morinda citrifolia*) leaf and roasted over a fire. An infusion of the crushed leaves is occasionally taken as a potion for treating various kinds of inflammation (*mūmū*), a remedy also reported from Tonga. The same medicine, or one made from the scraped bark, is occasionally taken as a potion for treating postpartum sickness (*failele gau*) and internal injuries (*gau*).

## ALOALO VAO

**SCIENTIFIC NAME:** *Mussaenda raiateensis* J. W. Moore
**FAMILY:** Rubiaceae (coffee family)
**ENGLISH NAME:** none

*Mussaenda raiateensis* is found on nearly every high island from Vanuatu (New Hebrides) to Tahiti. It is native to Samoa, where it occurs in open secondary vegetation in coastal and lowland areas, and is occasionally cultivated in villages for its medicinal properties.

**Aloalo vao** is a shrub or small tree up to 10 m in height, but usually much shorter. The simple, oppositely arranged leaves have an ovate to elliptic blade 7—25 cm long. The flowers are numerous in terminal clusters, each with a single ovate, white, leaflike sepal 5—12 cm long. The yellow, tubular corolla is 2.5—3.5 cm long with five spreading lobes. The fruit is an ellipsoid berry 10—18 mm long, brown with lighter colored spots at maturity.

USES: An infusion of the crushed leaves or scraped bark is very commonly taken as a potion, or a mixture of the crushed leaves and coconut oil or water is used as a massage for treating a type of inflammation called *mūmū tatau*, and less commonly for *mūmū lele*.

## ALOE

**SCIENTIFIC NAME:** *Aloe vera* L.
**FAMILY:** Agavaceae (yucca family)
**ENGLISH NAME:** aloe vera

*Aloe vera* is native to North Africa, but is now cultivated throughout the tropics and subtropics. In Polynesia, it had, until recently, been reported only from Hawai'i and Tonga, but has rapidly spread to the other island groups. In Samoa, it is mostly grown in pots or in houseyard gardens, but its popularity began only as recently as the

1980s. The medicinal use of aloe dates back to before the time of Alexander the Great (4th century B.C.), and is even mentioned in the New Testament of the Bible (John 19:39), originally for its use as a purgative.

Aloe is a succulent herb forming a rosette from a short, thick stem. The simple, alternately arranged leaves are succulent and spiny-margined, with a lanceolate blade 20—60 cm long tapering to a point from the broad base. The tubular, reflexed flowers are on an erect, long-stalked raceme up to 1 m in height, and have three outer red to orange sepals and three inner yellow petals 20—33 mm long. The fruit is a brown capsule 15—25 mm long at maturity.

USES: The sap from the fleshy leaves is very commonly applied as first aid for treating cuts (*lavea*) and, to a lesser extent, burns (*mū*). These uses, especially the latter one, are now common throughout the world. The sap, drunk fresh or boiled, is occasionally taken for a number of serious internal ailments such as asthma (*sela*) and cancer (*kanesa*).

## AOA

SCIENTIFIC NAME: *Ficus obliqua* Forst. f.
FAMILY: Moraceae (mulberry family)
ENGLISH NAMES: Polynesian banyan, strangler fig

*Ficus obliqua* is native from New Caledonia to Niue, and in Samoa is most commonly found in lowland to montane forest, where it often towers over the canopy. It begins life as an epiphyte, sends aerial roots to the ground, and eventually becomes a huge banyan tree with a spreading crown and a composite trunk composed of the fused and enlarged aerial roots, which have long since enveloped and "strangled" the "host" tree. Another very similar banyan, *Ficus prolixa* Forst. f., is used in the same ways. Both are called **aoa**, but some people distinguish the former as **aoa tane** (male banyan) and the latter as **aoa fafine** (female banyan).

Aoa is a giant banyan tree up to 30 m in height, with milky sap and the stem tip protected by a deciduous cap. The simple, alternately arranged, leathery leaves have an elliptic to lanceolate blade 6—15 cm long. The tiny flowers are enclosed within a globose receptacle. The fruit is a globose, orange, berrylike "syconium" 5—7 mm in diameter.

USES: The hanging roots are the only part of the plant used in Samoan medicine. An infusion of the crushed or scraped roots is occasionally taken as a potion for treating urinary tract problems (*tulitā*) and stomachache (*manava tīgā*).

## 'APU 'INITIA

SCIENTIFIC NAME: *Anacardium occidentale* L.
FAMILY: Anacardiaceae (cashew family)
ENGLISH NAMES: cashew, cashew nut

*Anacardium occidentale* is originally native to tropical America, but is now pantropic in cultivation. It is grown for its tasty seed, the cashew, which must be roasted before being eaten. In Samoa it is occasional in cultivation around houses, but does not grow wild. The name literally means "Indian apple," because the swollen stalk of the fruit is somewhat apple-like and is eaten (instead of the cashew) in Samoa.

'Apu 'Initia is a shrub or small tree up to 3 m or more in height. The simple, alternately arranged, glabrous leaves have a mostly obovate blade up to 20 cm long. The flowers are borne in short terminal panicles. The 5-parted, pinkish yellow to red flowers are about 8 mm in diameter and have 8—10 stamens. The oblong, red, fleshy, fruitlike stalk is 5—7 cm long, upon which sits the kidney-shaped fruit containing the seed (the cashew nut).

USES: The fruit is occasionally chewed and the juice swallowed for treating sore throat (*fa'a'ī a'ala*) and mouth infections (*pala gutu*). A similar use is also reported from the Philippines (de Padua *et al.* 1977).

## ATEATE
## (LAU ATEATE)

SCIENTIFIC NAME: *Wollastonia biflora* (L.) DC.
FAMILY: Asteraceae or Compositae (sunflower family)
ENGLISH NAME: beach sunflower

*Wollastonia biflora* is native from tropical Asia to eastern Polynesia. It is dispersed by means of its saltwater-resistant fruits, and is restricted mostly to littoral and coastal areas of high islands, often being the dominant species in dense, scrubby vegetation on exposed coastal slopes and cliffs. It is also frequently encountered as a weed in coastal coconut plantations in Samoa. The plant, until recently, was called *Wedelia biflora*.

Ateate is a branching, trailing to erect herbaceous subshrub 50—200 cm in height. The oppositely arranged, simple leaves have an ovate blade mostly 8—20 cm long, palmately veined from the base and pubescent or rough on both surfaces. The flowers are in sunflowerlike heads. The ray florets are strap-shaped and yellow, and the disc florets are numerous, tubular, and yellow. The fruiting heads are subglobose, 8—15 mm across, brown, and contain small, black, wedge-shaped seeds.

USES: An infusion of the crushed leaves is commonly taken as a potion for treating urinary tract problems (*tulitā*). Less frequently, the infusion is taken for treating fever with jaundice (*fiva samasama*) and stomachache (*manava tīgā*).

## 'AUTE SAMOA

SCIENTIFIC NAME: *Hibiscus rosa-sinensis* L.
FAMILY: Malvaceae (mallow family)
ENGLISH NAME: red hibiscus

*Hibiscus rosa-sinensis* is native to subtropical or tropical Asia, but has long been cultivated elsewhere in Asia and was carried in ancient times as far eastward as the Marquesas Islands. Many varieties and colors of this species exist, but the one used in Samoan medicine, **'aute Samoa**, has a double row of short, dark red petals. It is occasional around houses, sometimes in plantations, and even in mature forest (where it is a relict of former cultivation, since it does not produce seeds).

**'Aute Samoa** is a much-branched shrub up to 4 m in height. The simple, alternately arranged leaves have an ovate blade 6—15 cm long with toothed margins. The flowers are solitary in the leaf axils, on long stalks. The showy red corolla usually has 10 dark red petals up to 5 cm long. The numerous stamens are fused into a column that surrounds the long style. The fruit does not form.

**USES:** In a common folk remedy, the leaves are chewed and the mass applied to boils (*ma'i sua* and *sila'ilagi*), and to infected wounds (*'oloā*) thought to be caused by the bite of a ghost called Nifoloa. An infusion of the crushed leaves is sometimes taken as a potion for treating various kinds of inflammation *(mūmū)*. A similar use for treating wounds is reported from the Philippines (de Padua *et al.* 1978).

<h2 style="text-align:center">'AVA<br>('AVA SAMOA)</h2>

**SCIENTIFIC NAME:** *Piper methysticum* Forst. f.
**FAMILY:** Piperaceae (pepper family)
**ENGLISH NAME:** kava

*Piper methysticum* is native to Melanesia, but was introduced throughout the high islands of Polynesia by ancient voyagers. It thrives in wet, somewhat shady places, but in Samoa is found only in cultivation, usually in inland plantations. Since only male plants are known, kava is unable to reproduce itself sexually and must be propagated by man. It has long been used in Samoa and the rest of Polynesia to prepare a mildly narcotic beverage known by the same name. The grated, crushed, or chewed roots, which contain several active lactones, are mixed with water to produce a drink that looks like weak coffee and has a peppery taste numbing to the mouth and tongue. In sufficient quantities, it is mildly paralyzing and creates a euphoric but clear-minded state. In Samoa it has been drunk mostly in traditional ceremonies (kava ceremonies), but today men can be seen drinking it daily in the open markets of Apia and Salelologa.

Kava is a woody shrub up to 4 m in height. The green stems have swollen nodes, and arise from a woody rootstock. The simple, alternately arranged leaves have a heart-shaped blade 9—13-veined from the base and up to 30 cm long. The male flowers are arranged in solitary, axillary, greenish white spikes up to 6 cm long, arising from an axil opposite a leaf. The female flowers and fruits are unknown (except in Vanuatu, where both male and female plants occur).

**USES:** An infusion of the pounded root (i.e., kava drink) is often taken as a potion for treating stomachache (*manava tīgā*), backache (*tua tīgā*), and other body pains. The same infusion is occasionally used for treating venereal disease (*ma'i afi*) and urinary tract problems (*tulitā*). Kava is known in the Western World as an analgesic (painkiller), an antidiuretic (causing frequent urination), and a mild narcotic, and is imported into Europe, where it is used to make commercial medicines. Medicinal uses for the plant have been reported throughout Polynesia.

## 'AVA'AVAAITU
## ('AVA'AVAAITU TŪ)

**SCIENTIFIC NAME:** *Macropiper puberulum* (Benth.) Benth.
**FAMILY:** Piperaceae (pepper family)
**ENGLISH NAME:** none

*Macropiper puberulum* is native to Fiji, western Polynesia, and Rapa in eastern Polynesia. It is uncommon in lowland to montane forest in Samoa, but at high elevations is replaced by a related species, *Macropiper timothianum* A.C. Sm. The only uses reported for these plants are medicinal. The name **'ava'avaaitu,** which literally means "small ghost-kava," also refers to another related viney species, *Piper graeffei* Warb. To distinguish between the two, the former is called **'ava'avaaitu tū** (standing), and the latter **'ava'avaaitu sosolo** (climbing).

**'Ava'avaaitu** is a shrub mostly 50—150 cm in height. The simple, alternately arranged leaves have an ovate to heart-shaped blade 8—23 cm long, with 5—9 veins radiating out from the base. The flowers are in long, solitary, axillary spikes on separate female and male plants. The male spikes are white and the female ones are green. The numerous tiny red, fleshy fruits, about 1.5 mm in diameter, entirely cover the female spike.

**USES:** The plant is believed to have supernatural effects. An infusion of the leaves is often used as a potion for treating "ghost sickness" (*ma'i aitu*), and is also used in massage of ailments such as swellings (*fula*) and inflammations (*mūmū*) that are believed to be caused by the presence or actions of ghosts (*sāua* ailments). The plant is used similarly in Tonga for treating inflammation.

## 'AVAPUI
## (FĀUA POVI)

**SCIENTIFIC NAME:** *Zingiber zerumbet* (L.) Sm.
**FAMILY:** Zingiberaceae (ginger family)
**ENGLISH NAMES:** wild ginger, shampoo ginger

*Zingiber zerumbet* is native to tropical Asia, perhaps originally to India or Ceylon, but has long been cultivated in Southeast Asia and was carried by ancient voyagers across the Pacific as far east as Hawai'i. In Samoa, it is naturalized in old secondary forests, often forming dense stands, particularly in and around old habitations and on ridge trails. The whole plant is aromatic, and the clear, mildly scented fluid that collects in the bracts of the inflorescence was sprinkled onto the hair as a shampoo.

'Avapui is an erect herb 1 m or more in height, arising from a thickened underground rhizome. The leaves are borne in two vertical rows, with a lanceolate blade mostly 10—25 cm long. The flowers are in terminal, conelike spikes 6—10 cm long on a leafless stalk, and have green to red, rounded and overlapping bracts. The white to pale yellow, six-parted perianth (corolla plus calyx) is 3—5 cm long and has a single stamen. Only one flower forms per bract, and only one or two are open at a time. The fruit is a small, inconspicuous capsule enclosed within the bract.

**USES:** An infusion of the crushed roots is occasionally taken as a potion for treating various body pains (*tīgā*).

## ESI

**SCIENTIFIC NAME:** *Carica papaya* L.
**FAMILY:** Caricaceae (papaya family)
**ENGLISH NAMES:** papaya, pawpaw

*Carica papaya* is native to tropical America, but is now distributed throughout the tropics. It was an early European introduction to Polynesia and quickly spread to nearly every high island in the region. Papaya is cultivated around houses and in plantations in Samoa for its delicious fruit, and often escapes to secondary forest and waste places.

**Esi** is a palmlike, soft-wooded, usually unbranched tree up to 10 m in height, with a copious, milky sap. The simple, alternately arranged leaves are at the top of the trunk, and have a round, palmately 7—11-lobed blade up to 30 cm or more in diameter, borne on a long petiole. The unisexual flowers are borne on separate male and female trees; the male flowers, with a cream-colored tubular corolla 2—3 cm long, are in hanging panicles, and the female flowers are solitary and axillary with a cream-colored corolla 4—6 cm wide. The fruit is a large, variously shaped, yellow to orange berry containing a thick, red-to-orange pulp with numerous round, black seeds on its inner wall.

**USES:** This is of minor medicinal use in Samoa. An infusion of the scraped inner bark is sometimes taken as a mouth rinse or gargle for treating toothache (*nifo tīgā*).

## FA'I

**SCIENTIFIC NAME:** *Musa* x *paradisiaca* L.
**FAMILY:** Musaceae (banana family)
**ENGLISH NAMES:** banana, plantain

*Musa* x *paradisiaca* is a complex of bananas and plantains that originated somewhere in the Indo-Malaysian area from hybrids between two other species. There has been much confusion in the taxonomy of this plant, and nowadays the numerous varieties are grouped according to the genetic make-up (i.e., AAAB has 3/4 genes from *Musa acuminata* and 1/4 from *Musa balbisiana*, while AABB has half of each). Many named varieties are found in Samoa, some brought by ancient Polynesians, others by Europeans.

Fa'i is a large treelike herb up to 5 m or more in height. The leaves are spirally arranged and their bases together form the fleshy "trunk." The leaf blade is large and oblong, with finely parallel veins from the thick midrib. The flowers are in massive racemes with large, brightly colored bracts. The corolla is composed of 3 orange petals and similar petal-like sepals. The fruit is a large, spindle-shaped berry that is green or yellow at maturity, the green ones often being eaten cooked and the yellow ones eaten raw. Seeds are not produced, but the plant reproduces by means of suckers forming at the base of the trunk.

**USES:** The sap from the trunk of the *mamae* variety is occasionally given to infants to treat an ailment called *ila fale*. The crushed or chewed leaves are sometimes applied to wounds (*lavea*) and burns (*mū*).

## FASA
## (LAU FALA)

**SCIENTIFIC NAME:** *Pandanus tectorius* Parkinson
**FAMILY:** Pandanaceae (screwpine family)
**ENGLISH NAMES:** screwpine, pandanus

*Pandanus tectorius*, in its broadest sense, is native to most of Polynesia, but so many other "species" have been named from the area that it is difficult to delineate ranges. Several kinds of pandanus are recognized in Samoa, one of them growing wild in littoral forest, another two in montane forest and scrub, and many others cultivated around houses and in plantations (**lau fala, totolo**). The leaves are used for making mats, baskets, and fans, and formerly, items such as sails, sandals, and even clothing. The related, cultivated screwpine, **paogo** (*Pandanus whitmeeanus* Mart.), is sometimes used interchangeably in medicinal applications.

Fasa is a stout, sparsely branched tree up to 10 m in height, but usually much less. The trunk is armed with numerous sharp to blunt prickles, marked by ringlike leaf scars, and is often supported by aerial prop roots. The stiff, coarse, swordlike leaves up to 1.5 m long are arranged in tight spirals at the ends of the branches; the margins and lower surface of the midrib are usually armed with prickles. The male and female flowers are on different trees: the white male flowers are numerous in hanging racemes bearing several large, white, fragrant bracts, and the female flowers are in a compound, globose structure with the ovaries forming the "keys." The fruit is a large, woody, subglobose "syncarp" with numerous (often 50 or more) woody keys.

**USES:** An infusion of the crushed pith from the prop roots is sometimes given as a potion for treating stomachache (*manava tīgā*), food poisoning (*'ōnā*), and less commonly for urinary tract problems (*tulitā*).

## FAU
## (FAU TŪ)

**SCIENTIFIC NAME:** *Hibiscus tiliaceus* L.
**FAMILY:** Malvaceae (mallow family)
**ENGLISH NAME:** beach hibiscus

*Hibiscus tiliaceus* is a wide-ranging tree found in both the Old and New World tropics. It is native throughout Polynesia, and is common on beaches, in disturbed places, secondary forest, and on the margins of estuaries and swamps in Samoa. Its soft, easily worked wood is often fashioned into outrigger floats, house parts, and tool handles, and is a favorite for firewood. Also of great utility are the inner bark fibers that are (or were) used for making fishing lines, nets, mats, and ropes.

**Fau** is a medium-sized tree up to 15 m in height, erect with a broad crown or forming dense thickets with its low, spreading branches. The simple, alternately arranged leaves have a heart-shaped blade mostly 8—20 cm long. The flowers have a corolla of five petals 5—8 cm long, lemon yellow with purple at the base, and the stamens are united into a tube. The fruit is a subglobose capsule mostly 15—25 mm wide, containing about 15 seeds that are released when the capsule splits open.

**USES:** This plant is of minor medicinal use in Samoa. The slimy sap from the inner bark is sometimes applied to cuts in folk medicine, and is applied as eyedrops to treat eye injuries (*mata pa'ia*), but *Kleinhovia hospita* (**fu'afu'a**) is much more commonly used for these purposes. The crushed young leaves are sometimes applied to burns. A similar eye remedy is reported from Tonga.

## FETAU

**SCIENTIFIC NAME:** *Calophyllum inophyllum* L.
**FAMILY:** Clusiaceae or Guttiferae (mangosteen family)
**ENGLISH NAMES:** calophyllum, Alexandrian laurel

*Calophyllum inophyllum* is widely distributed from tropical East Africa to eastern Polynesia, and although its floating fruits are well-adapted to seawater dispersal, it may be a Polynesian introduction to the eastern part of its range. The tree occurs in coastal areas, particularly on rocky, cliff-bound coasts and coastal slopes, where it is often the dominant species, and it is sometimes planted as an ornamental in coastal villages. The hard, fine-grained wood is easily worked with stone or metal tools, and for this reason it is highly esteemed in Samoa and the rest of Polynesia.

**Fetau** is a large tree up to 25 m in height, with four-angled stems, deeply furrowed and cracked bark, and sticky, yellow sap. The simple, oppositely arranged leaves have a finely veined, elliptic to ovate blade 10—25 cm long. The flowers, arranged in short racemes, are 15—30 mm across, and have four white petals, four similar white sepals, and numerous yellow stamens. The fruit is a globose to ovoid drupe mostly 3—4 cm across, green at maturity and containing a single oily seed enclosed within a hard, bony shell.

USES: A solution of the crumpled leaves is sometimes used as an eyewash for treating eye injuries (*mata pa'ia*) and blurry vision (*mata puaoa*). This is probably an ancient Polynesian practice that is also reported from Tonga and as far away as the Philippines (de Padua *et al.* 1981). An infusion of the leaves, boiled or not, is sometimes taken as a potion for treating diarrhea (*manava tatā*).

## FILIMOTO

**SCIENTIFIC NAME:** *Flacourtia rukam* Zoll. & Mor. ex Mor.
**FAMILY:** Flacourtiaceae (flacourtia family)
**ENGLISH NAME:** Indian plum

*Flacourtia rukam* ranges from Malaysia to Polynesia, and although it is apparently native to Samoa, it is a recent introduction to Fiji, where it is known only in cultivation. It is occasional in secondary forest and disturbed areas in Samoa, where the fruits are sometimes made into a jam.
    **Filimoto** is a medium-sized tree up to 15 m in height, with somewhat zigzag stems. The simple, alternately arranged leaves have an ovate to elliptic blade 5—15 cm long with toothed margins. The unisexual flowers are in short axillary racemes, with separate male and female trees. The small flowers lack a corolla, and the male flowers are composed most conspicuously of many spreading white stamens. The fleshy, red, globose, several-seeded fruit is mostly 2—2.5 cm in diameter.

USES: An infusion of the scraped bark is sometimes taken as a potion for treating various kinds of inflammation (*mūmū*), and a mixture of the crushed leaves in coconut oil is sometimes applied to skin sores (*matolo* and *papala*).

## FĪSOA

**SCIENTIFIC NAME:** *Colubrina asiatica* (L.) Brongn.
**FAMILY:** Rhamnaceae (buckthorn family)
**ENGLISH NAME:** none

*Colubrina asiatica* ranges from tropical East Africa to Hawai'i, and is found on all the major high islands of Polynesia. It is common on sandy and rocky beaches in Samoa, and is sometimes almost vinelike as it climbs into the canopy of littoral forest. The leaves, which contain chemicals known as saponins that produce a lather in water, were formerly used for soap in Samoa and elsewhere in the Pacific.
    **Fīsoa** is a sprawling shrub with the somewhat zigzag stems. The simple, alternately arranged leaves have an ovate, glossy green blade 3—12 cm long and somewhat 3-

veined from the base. The tiny flowers are arranged in short axillary cymes. The corolla has five yellow petals 1—2 mm long. The fruit is a globose, 3-seeded capsule 6—10 mm in diameter, brown and papery at maturity.

**USES:** An infusion of the leaves, boiled or not, is very commonly taken as a potion for treating postpartum sickness (*failele gau*).

## F I U

**SCIENTIFIC NAME:** *Zingiber officinale* Roscoe
**FAMILY:** Zingiberaceae (ginger family)
**ENGLISH NAME:** ginger

*Zingiber officinale* is native to somewhere in tropical Asia, but has now been distributed throughout the tropics. It is a European introduction to Samoa, where it is occasional in cultivation around houses and in plantations. The rhizome is used as a spice in cooking.

Fiu is an erect herb up to 75 cm in height, arising from a fleshy, creeping, underground rhizome (the ginger "root"). The lower leaves are reduced and sheat-like, and the upper ones are arranged in two rows. The blade is narrowly lanceolate with parallel veins from the midrib. The flowers are arranged in spikes on bract-bearing, leafless stems. The corolla has six tepals (petals and similar petal-like sepals) that are yellow with purple and cream-colored markings. The fruit is a capsule, but rarely forms in Samoa.

**USES:** An infusion of the crushed or scraped rhizome is very commonly taken as a potion for treating stomachache (*manava tīgā* and *manava oso*). A similar use is reported from the Philippines (de Padua *et al.* 1978). It is also sometimes taken for treating stomatitis (*pala gutu*) and respiratory difficulties (*sela*).

## FU‘AFU‘A

**SCIENTIFIC NAME:** *Kleinhovia hospita* L.
**FAMILY:** Sterculiaceae (cacao family)
**ENGLISH NAME:** none

*Kleinhovia hospita* is native from tropical Africa eastward to Tahiti, and is a common tree in secondary forest and plantations in the lowlands of Samoa. The wood is sometimes used for construction, and, when rubbed with a harder stick, to start fires. The folded leaves are used for holding grated bark or crushed leaves used for medicine.

Fu‘afu‘a is a large spreading tree up to 20 m in height. The simple, alternately arranged leaves have a heart-shaped blade 5—24 cm long. The flowers are arranged in large, freely branched, terminal panicles. The corolla has four pink petals 7—10 mm long, with shorter, colored sepals. The fruit is a pink, inflated, papery, 5-lobed capsule 12—24 mm in diameter, containing five white seeds.

**USES:** The sap scraped from the inner bark is commonly applied as first aid to cuts and wounds (*manu'a* and *lavea*) to staunch the bleeding. The sap is also occasionally dripped into the eyes to treat eye injuries (*mata pa'ia*) and irritations (*ma'i mata*).

## FUE LAUFAO

**SCIENTIFIC NAME:** *Epipremnum pinnatum* (L.) Engl.
**FAMILY:** Araceae (aroid family)
**ENGLISH NAME:** none

*Epipremnum pinnatum* is native from tropical Asia to eastern Polynesia, but a variegated type is now widespread in cultivation in the tropics. The native type is commonly found sprawling on the forest floor and climbing tree trunks in relatively undisturbed lowland to montane forest in Samoa. The tough roots were formerly used to make basketlike fish traps (*'enu*).

**Fue laufao** is a creeping vine that, upon encountering a tree, climbs the trunk and grows up into the canopy, adhering to the tree by means of numerous roots emanating from the stem. The large, simple, alternately arranged leaves have an elliptic blade up to 50 cm long, usually with a deeply split margin. The inflorescence is a large cylindrical spadix covered with tiny sessile, apetalous flowers and surrounded by a large, white deciduous spathe. The fruits are several-sided and flat on top, and cover the surface of the spadix.

**USES:** An infusion of the scraped roots or stems is occasionally taken as a potion for treating *mūmū ta'ai* and other types of inflammation (*mūmū*).

## FUE MANOGI
## ('AVA'AVAAITU SOSOLO)

**SCIENTIFIC NAME:** *Piper graeffei* Warb.
**FAMILY:** Piperaceae (pepper family)
**ENGLISH NAME:** none

*Piper graeffei* is endemic to Samoa, where it is found on all the main islands. It is common in undisturbed lowland and montane forest up to an elevation of about 900 m. When young, it creeps along the ground, and in this state it is often called **'ava'avaaitu** or **'ava'avaaitu sosolo** ("creeping ghosts' kava"). When it encounters a tree, it grows up the trunk until it becomes a thick vine, when it is usually called **fue manogi**, because of its fragrant leaves and stems.

**Fue manogi** is a trunk climber with prominent nodes and roots along its stems that adhere to tree bark. The simple, alternately arranged leaves have an ovate to heart-shaped blade 8—16 cm long with 5—7 veins radiating from the base. The tiny green, unisexual flowers are borne in long narrow spikes that develop opposite a leaf. These lack petals and sepals, and occur on separate male and female plants. The male spikes are cream-colored from the pollen, and the female spikes, when mature, are covered with tiny red, fleshy fruits about 1 mm in diameter.

**USES:** An infusion from the scraped bark is commonly taken as a potion for treating mouth infections (*pala gutu*) and coughs (*tale*). The plant is believed to have supernatural healing properties, and like *'ava 'avaaitu tū*, the juice from the crushed leaves, often with those of other several other plant species, is occasionally applied to the skin for treating "ghost sickness" (*ma'i aitu*), inflammation (*mūmū*) that is thought to have supernatural origins, and infected wounds (*'oloā*) thought to have been caused by the bite of the ghost known as Nifoloa.

## FUE MOA
## (FUEFUE MOA)

**SCIENTIFIC NAME:** *Ipomoea pes-caprae* (L.) R. Br.
**FAMILY:** Convolvulaceae (morning-glory family)
**ENGLISH NAME:** beach morning-glory

*Ipomoea pes-caprae* is found throughout the tropics, and grows on all the high islands in the tropical Pacific. It and the beach pea (**fue sina**) are the two most common and characteristic vines on Samoan beaches, particularly on sandy shores, where one or both species typically dominate the beach down to the hightide mark. Few uses, other than medicinal applications, are reported for it.

**Fue moa** is a prostrate vine with purple stems that form roots at the nodes. The simple, oppositely arranged leaves are thick and fleshy, with an oval blade 3—10 cm long notched at the tip (and looking like the footprint of a goat, hence the Latin name "pes-caprae"—goat's foot). The flowers are solitary or in few-flowered cymes in the leaf axils. The showy pink to rose-purple, funnel-shaped corolla is 3—5 cm long. The fruit is an ovoid capsule 12—17 mm long, containing four hairy seeds.

**USES:** The sap from the young leaves is sometimes dripped into the eyes for treating eye problems (*ma'i mata*).

## FUE SAINA

**SCIENTIFIC NAME:** *Mikania micrantha* H.B.K.
**FAMILY:** Asteraceae or Compositae (sunflower family)
**ENGLISH NAME:** mile-a-minute weed

*Mikania micrantha* is native to tropical America, but has now been established as a weed on many islands of the tropical Pacific. It is the most common weed in Samoa, where it can occur from near the shore to the tops of the highest mountains, and can completely dominate disturbed areas and plantations. Another plant found in Micronesia, *Mikania scandens* (L.) Willd., may be the same species; if so, the latter is the correct name for the species. The mile-a-minute weed was introduced sometime after the turn of the century when the first groups of Chinese arrived, hence the origin of its Samoan name (=Chinese weed).

Fue Saina is a twining herbaceous vine that often climbs over low vegetation and up into trees. The simple, oppositely arranged leaves have a heart-shaped blade 5—10 cm long with wavy margins. The flowers are arranged in heads in dense terminal and axillary inflorescences. The heads are surrounded by 5 bracts and contain four white, tubular flowers 3—5 mm long. The fruit is a tiny achene about 2 mm long with a dense terminal plume of white bristles slightly longer than the fruit. These bristles allow the flowers to float for long distances in the wind.

USES: In one of the most common folk remedies in Samoa, the juice expressed from leaves rolled in the hands is dripped onto wounds (*lavea* and *manu'a*) to staunch the bleeding and to prevent infection. A similar use is reported from Fiji (Smith 1991) and de Padua *et al.* (1983).

## FUE SINA
## (FUEFUE SINA)

SCIENTIFIC NAME: *Vigna marina* (Burm.) Merr.
FAMILY: Fabaceae or Leguminosae (pea family)
ENGLISH NAME: beach pea

*Vigna marina* is widely distributed throughout the tropics, and is found on most tropical Pacific islands. It is a common component of sandy beaches of Samoa, often in combination with *Ipomoea pes-caprae* (**fue moa**), and is somewhat weedy in coastal coconut plantations. It is also sometimes found along inland roads, possibly spread there by seeds in beach sand used in road work.

Fue sina is a trailing, prostrate, herbaceous vine. The alternately arranged, trifoliate leaves have three rounded to ovate leaflets 4—10 cm long. The flowers are in axillary racemes up to 20 cm long, and have a yellow papilionaceous corolla 10—15 mm long. The fruit is a black, cylindrical pod 5—8 cm long that splits open along the two seams.

USES: This is one of the most frequently used plants for treating supernaturally induced ailments, particularly for ailments known as *sāua* that have no obvious origins and are thus attributed to supernatural causes. An infusion of the crushed leaves is very commonly given as a potion, dripped into the eyes, nose, mouth, and ears, or rubbed onto the skin, particularly of infants. It is used similarly in Tonga. The same medicine is commonly massaged onto the skin for treating inflammation (*mūmū*), probably for the same reason.

## FUTU

SCIENTIFIC NAME: *Barringtonia asiatica* (L.) Kurz
FAMILY: Barringtoniaceae (barringtonia family)
ENGLISH NAME: fish-poison tree

*Barringtonia asiatica* ranges from Madagascar to the Marquesas Islands, and is native to most of the high islands in the tropical Pacific, and even on some atolls. It is often the dominant tree on undisturbed rocky shores all around Samoa, often excluding nearly all other trees. The grated seed of the large fruit was formerly used as a fish poison.

**Futu** is a large, spreading tree up to 20 or more in height. The large, simple, alternately arranged, leathery leaves are crowded at the stem tips, with an obovate blade mostly 10—40 cm long. The flowers are arranged in short terminal racemes. The corolla consists of 4 white petals 6—10 cm long, surrounding numerous, long, showy white-and-pink stamens. The large, top-shaped fruit is 4-angled, 8—12 cm long, and green at maturity, with two persistent, leaflike sepals at the top.

**USES:** An infusion of the scraped seed is occasionally applied to skin sores (*papala*).

## GATAE
## (GATAE SAMOA)

**SCIENTIFIC NAME:** *Erythrina variegata* L.
**FAMILY:** Fabaceae or Leguminosae (pea family)
**ENGLISH NAME:** coral tree

*Erythrina variegata* (var. *orientalis*) is native from Zanzibar in the Indian Ocean to eastern Polynesia, but is now widely cultivated in the tropics. Its native habitat is littoral forest on rocky shores of high islands, and sometimes inland in coastal and ridge forests. It is also commonly cultivated, particularly a type (var. *fastigiata*) with ascending branches that make excellent "living fences." The soft, light wood has little use other than for fishnet floats and firewood. The related, introduced *Erythrina subumbrans* (Hassk.) Merr. (**gatae Pālagi** or dadap), is sometimes used medicinally in the same as as **gatae**.

**Gatae** is a spreading tree up to 20 m in height, with the trunk and branches coarsely spiny. The alternately arranged leaves are trifoliate, with three ovate to nearly round leaflets 4—25 cm long. The flowers are borne on axillary racemes up to 35 cm long, and have a showy, papilionaceous, orange-red corolla 4—6 cm long. The fruit is a curved, linear-oblong pod 12—22 cm long, containing 3—10 kidney-shaped seeds 10—15 mm long.

**USES:** The juice from the petiole is often dripped into injured eyes (*mata pa'ia*) and sties (*matafā*), and the scraped bark is applied as a plaster to swellings (*fula*). Cox and Balick (1994) noted that the bark has a chemical that inhibits the enzyme involved in inflammation (*mūmū*), but the plant is seldom used for this purpose in Samoa.

## IFI

**SCIENTIFIC NAME:** *Inocarpus fagifer* (Parkinson) Fosb.
**FAMILY:** Fabaceae or Leguminosae (pea family)
**ENGLISH NAME:** Tahitian chestnut

*Inocarpus fagifer* is distributed from Malaysia to the Marquesas Islands, but is probably an ancient introduction throughout Polynesia. It is casually cultivated in plantations, but is also occasionally naturalized in native forest, particularly in wet soil along streams and on the margins of mangrove swamps. The fruit contains a large, edible, peanutlike seed esteemed by Samoans; these are collected from the ground and roasted unopened on a fire, or the seeds are extracted and boiled.

**Ifi** is a large tree up to 15 m or more in height, with a strongly fluted and buttressed trunk. The simple, alternately arranged leaves have an elliptic to oblong blade up to 30 cm or more long. The flowers are in simple or branched axillary spikes, and bear a corolla of five white, linear petals mostly 6—10 mm long. The compressed, ovoid to obovoid, hard-shelled fruit is up to 10 cm in diameter and contains one large, edible seed.

**USES:** An infusion of the scraped bark is sometimes used as a potion for treating stomachache (*manava tīgā*). In Tonga, the bark is used to treat diarrhea.


# KUʻAVA

**SCIENTIFIC NAME:** *Psidium guajava* L.
**FAMILY:** Myrtaceae (myrtle family)
**ENGLISH NAME:** guava

*Psidium guajava* is native to tropical America, but is now widely distributed in the tropics. It was introduced to Polynesia in the 19th century, and soon became a serious weed of open, disturbed places such as pastures, plantations, roadsides, and fallow land. The fruit is edible fresh, but because of the numerous hard seeds, it is much more suitable for making jam or juice. Although originally introduced as a fruit tree, it is now also known for its medicinal properties, the knowledge of which has spread from island to island in the Pacific. Its medicinal value is due mainly to the presence of tannin (up to 10% dry weight) in the bark, leaves, and leaf buds, which makes it useful as an astringent.

**Kuʻava** is a shrub or small tree up to 10 m in height, with four-angled stems and bark that peels off in flakes. The simple, oppositely arranged leaves have an oval to elliptic blade 6—15 cm long. The flowers, borne singly in the leaf axils, have a corolla of five white petals 10—15 mm long and numerous showy white stamens. The fruit is a yellow, globose to ovoid berry 5—10 cm long, with many small, hard seeds embedded in the pink to yellow pulp.

**USES:** An infusion of the young leaves, or the juice from the chewed leaves, is commonly swallowed for treating stomachache (*manava tīgā*), a use also noted from Tonga. Less commonly, the same medicine is used for treating diarrhea (*manava tatā* and *tulatula*), a use well known in the Pacific, and for mouth infections (*pala gutu*).

# LĀʻAU FAI LAFA

**SCIENTIFIC NAME:** *Senna alata* (L.) Roxb.
**FAMILY:** Fabaceae or Leguminosae (pea family)
**ENGLISH NAMES:** candlebush, acapulco

*Senna alata*, until recently called *Cassia alata*, is native to the New World tropics, but was introduced into tropical Asia early in the European Era and was so commonly grown there that many authors considered it to be native to India. It is a recent European introduction to Samoa (perhaps around the 1920s) and is occasional in cultivation in villages and plantations, particularly in wet places.

**Lāʻau fai lafa** is a coarse, erect shrub up to 4 m in height. The alternately arranged, pinnately compound leaves have 8—14 oppositely arranged, oblong to ovate leaflets 6—15 cm long. The showy yellow flowers are crowded and overlapping in erect terminal racemes, each flower concealed in the bud by overlapping showy yellow bracts. The corolla has five obovate petals up to 2 cm long. The fruit is an oblong, black, somewhat papery pod mostly 10—15 cm long, winged on the angles.

**USES:** In one of the most common and best known folk remedies, the juice squeezed from the leaves is dripped onto ringworm (*lafa*). The plant is used similarly in Tonga, Fiji (Smith 1985), and the Philippines (de Padua *et al.* 1977).

# LAMA

**SCIENTIFIC NAME:** *Aleurites moluccana* (L.) Willd.
**FAMILY:** Euphorbiaceae (spurge family)
**ENGLISH NAME:** candlenut

*Aleurites moluccana* is probably native to the Malaysia area, but was carried by ancient seafarers throughout the Pacific islands as far east as Hawaiʻi. It is only occasionally found in native forest, such as at ʻAsau on Savaiʻi and on Nuʻutele off the east coast of ʻUpolu, but is also sometimes cultivated in villages. In ancient times, the roasted and shelled seeds, strung together on a skewer, were burned as a light source throughout Polynesia, hence the English name "candlenut." The soot from the burning nuts is used to produce the black dye applied to tapa cloth and for the ink employed in Polynesian tattooing.

**Lama** is a large tree up to 25 m in height, with young stems and foliage having a mealy surface with a characteristic gray-green color. The simple, alternately arranged leaves have an ovate to irregularly palmately-lobed blade 9—22 cm long. The unisexual flowers are in dense panicles. The white, five-lobed corolla is 5—10 mm long. The fruit is a green, subglobose drupe 3.5—4.5 cm long, containing a hard, bony shell enclosing the oily seed.

**USES:** The crushed seed is often rubbed onto sores on the skin (*papala*), on the head (*foe*, possibly impetigo), and on a skin fungus called *'utu*. An infusion of the scraped bark or crushed leaves is often taken as a potion for treating mouth sores *(gutu malū* and *pala gutu*) of infants (a use also reported from Tonga), or the chewed seed may be dripped into the mouth of the infant for the same reason.

## LAU 'AUTĀ
### (LAU MAGAMAGA, ALOFILIMA)

**SCIENTIFIC NAME:** *Phymatosorus scolopendria* (Burm. f.) Pichi Serm.
**FAMILY:** Polypodiaceae (common-fern family)
**ENGLISH NAME:** none

*Phymatosorus scolopendria* is a terrestrial or epiphytic fern ranging from tropical Africa to eastern Polynesia, and is native to Samoa. It is probably the most common and widespread fern in Polynesia, where it occurs in a wide variety of habitats—from coral rock crevices in littoral scrub vegetation to tree trunks in montane rain forest. Some botanists believe that the larger type occurring mostly on the ground belongs to a separate species, *Phymatosorus grossus*.

Lau 'autā is a creeping fern with stout, dark brown to black rhizomes bearing scattered, dark brown scales. The erect fronds are deeply pinnately divided into 1—8 pairs of lobes and are up to 40 cm long on a stipe of shorter or equal length. The round sori are arranged in two rows on either side of the midrib and are shallowly depressed into the frond to form a raised or bordered pit on the upper surface.

**USES:** This is one of the most widely used of all Samoan medicinal plants. Most commonly, an infusion of the scraped rhizome and/or crushed leaves is taken as a potion for treating various kinds of inflammation (*mūmū*). A similar use is reported from Tonga. An infusion of the crushed leaves is occasionally taken as a potion or is applied to the skin for treating infected, hard-to-cure wounds (*fāoailetā*). Less commonly, an infusion of the scraped rhizome and/or crushed leaves is taken as a potion for treating childhood ailments (*ila mea* and *ila fale*), stomachache (*manava tīgā*), and urinary tract problems (*tulitā*).

## LAU MAFIAFIA
### (LAU OLIVE, FUE SELELĀ, FUA SELELĀ, SUNI VAO)

**SCIENTIFIC NAME:** *Hoya australis* R. Br.
**FAMILY:** Asclepiadaceae (milkweed family)
**ENGLISH NAME:** wax plant

*Hoya australis* is native from Vanuatu (New Hebrides) and Australia eastward to Samoa. This wide distribution can be attributed to its plumed seeds that are carried long distances in air currents. *Hoya* is most commonly found climbing over low vegetation in littoral areas and as an epiphyte in coastal to lowland forest, but occasionally occurs in forest and scrub vegetation at up to 600 m elevation. The plant makes an attractive ornamental, but is infrequently used in this way.

**Lau mafiafia** is a semi-woody, climbing or prostrate vine (becoming epiphytic in forests) with a milky sap. The simple, oppositely arranged leaves have a thick, fleshy, elliptic to rounded blade 5—15 cm long. The waxy white flowers are red in the center, 13—18 mm in diameter, and are borne in axillary umbels. The fruit is a pointed, narrow, cylindrical follicle up to 15 cm long, splitting along one side to release the numerous plumed seeds.

**USES:** An infusion of the crushed leaves is commonly taken as a potion or is applied to the skin for treating various kinds of inflammation (*mūmū*), a use also reported from Tonga. The leaves are often used as an applicator for spreading coconut cream onto skin sores (*matolo*) that usually occur on the head, and an infusion of the crushed leaves is taken as a potion for treating various internal pains (*to'ala, moa tīgā*, etc.).

## LAU PATA
## (LAU PAPATA, PATA)

**SCIENTIFIC NAME:** *Macaranga harveyana* (Muell. Arg.) Muell. Arg.
**FAMILY:** Euphorbiaceae (spurge family)
**ENGLISH NAME:** none

*Macaranga harveyana* ranges from Fiji to the Society Islands and is native to Samoa, where it is common in disturbed forests and waste places, frequently as the dominant species in old plantations that have been abandoned for several years. It has a soft wood that is of little use other than as firewood.

**Lau pata** is a small, spreading tree 3—8 m in height. The simple, alternately arranged leaves have an ovate blade 12—26 cm long with a long petiole joining it inside the margin (i.e., it is peltate), with about eight veins radiating to the blade margin from that point. The tiny, yellow or green, apetalous (without petals) flowers are unisexual, in branching axillary panicles (male) or racemes (female) on separate male and female trees. The fruit is a subglobose capsule 6—10 mm in diameter, and is covered with scattered, soft spines 3—8 mm long.

**USES:** An infusion of the scraped bark is sometimes taken as a potion for treating internal ailments such as a digestive tract disorders (*fe'efe'e*), intestinal worms (*'anufe*), and urinary tract problems (*tulitā*), acting as a purgative.

## LAU TĪ
## (TĪ)

**SCIENTIFIC NAME:** *Cordyline fruticosa* (L.) Chev.
**FAMILY:** Agavaceae (yucca family)
**ENGLISH NAMES:** ti, ti plant

*Cordyline fruticosa*, formerly known as *Cordyline terminalis*, is probably native to tropical Asia, but is now widely distributed across the Pacific and is cultivated throughout the tropics and subtropics. It was probably an ancient introduction to Samoa, where a number of local varieties have long been cultivated, and is now completely naturalized there as an understory shrub of primary and disturbed forests. Ti has, since ancient times, played a large part in the Polynesian material culture. The leaves are or were commonly employed in making skirts, dance costumes, roofing thatch, and food wrappers. Also of importance were the large, sugar-laden, tuberous roots that were baked in underground ovens.

Lau ti is a sparsely branching shrub up to 5 m in height, growing from an enlarged tuber. The spirally arranged leaves are in clusters at the ends of the stems, and have a lanceolate to oblong blade 30—70 cm long with the parallel veins forming a shallow angle with the midrib. The flowers are in compound spikes with a leaflike bract at the base. The three petals and three sepals are similar, 8—14 mm long, and white, pink, or purple. The red to purple fruit is a globose, three-parted berry up to 8 mm in diameter.

**USES:** The leaves dipped in water are very commonly used by both healers and lay people to massage various kinds of inflammation (*mūmū*), headaches (*ulu tīgā*) and other body aches, and for general massage.

## LEVA

**SCIENTIFIC NAME:** *Cerbera manghas* L.
**FAMILY:** Apocynaceae (dogbane family)
**ENGLISH NAME:** none

*Cerbera manghas* is distributed from the Seychelle Islands in the Indian Ocean eastward to the Marquesas Islands, and is occasional to uncommon on rocky or sandy shores of Samoa. It has a patchy distribution in Polynesia, and on many islands the related *Cerbera odollam* is found instead. This latter species is also found in Samoa, mostly on the north side of Savai'i. The fruit of the two species is reported to be poisonous, and the flowers are sometimes used for decoration.

Leva is a small to medium-sized tree up to 12 m in height, with a milky sap. The glossy leaves are arranged in a tight spiral at the ends of the branches, and have an elliptic blade 9—20 cm long. The flowers are in long terminal cymes. The showy white corolla has a narrow tube 2.5—4.5 cm long and a red throat with five spreading lobes perpendicular to it. The dry, fibrous fruit is similar to a mango fruit in size and shape, and is red at maturity. *Cerbera odollam* differs most significantly in having a yellow "eye" at the center of the corolla, rather than red.

**USES:** The crushed leaves mixed with coconut oil are often applied to skin sores (*po'u*) and fungal skin infections such as *'utu, lafa,* and *tane*.

## MA'ANUNU

**SCIENTIFIC NAME:** *Tarenna sambucina* (Forst. f.) Durand
**FAMILY:** Rubiaceae (coffee family)
**ENGLISH NAME:** none

*Tarenna sambucina* is native from Vanuatu to the Marquesas Islands, and is found on most of the high islands in this region. It is occasional in scrub forest, open secondary forest, and in disturbed places in the lowlands and foothills of Samoa.

**Ma'anunu** is a small tree up to 6 m or more in height, with stems 4-angled when young. The simple, oppositely arranged leaves have an elliptic blade 6—18 cm long. The flowers are in dense, widely branching, terminal cymose clusters. The tubular, yellowish to white corolla has five spreading lobes about 6 mm long. The fruit is a globose berry about 5 mm in diameter, black at maturity.

**USES:** An infusion of the scraped bark is often taken as a potion for treating a kind of inflammation called *mūmū tua'ula*.


## MAGELE

**SCIENTIFIC NAME:** *Trema cannabina* Lour.
**FAMILY:** Ulmaceae (elm family)
**ENGLISH NAME:** none

*Trema cannabina* is distributed from India to western Polynesia and is native to Samoa, where it is occasional in disturbed places. Its only reported uses in Samoa are medicinal.

**Magele** is a small, slender tree up to 8 m or more in height. The simple, alternately arranged leaves have an ovate to lanceolate blade 6—12 cm long, with rough (scabrous) surfaces, serrate margins, and a cordate base with unequal sides. The flowers are in short, axillary, cymose clusters up to 2 cm long. The greenish white perianth (which lacks petals) is about 1 mm long. The fruit is an ovoid drupe 1.5—3 mm long, red-brown to black at maturity.

**USES:** An infusion of the scraped bark or other plant parts is sometimes taken as a potion for treating mouth infections (*pala gutu*) and coughs (*tale*).


## MAGO

**SCIENTIFIC NAME:** *Mangifera indica* L.
**FAMILY:** Anacardiaceae (cashew family)
**ENGLISH NAME:** mango

*Mangifera indica* is probably native to India or Burma, but is now cultivated throughout the tropics. It was an early European introduction to Polynesia, where it is commonly grown in villages and plantations. It is not reported to be naturalized in Samoa, and trees found in forests are relicts of former cultivation. The tree is grown for its delicious, highly esteemed, edible fruit. An oil in the skin of the fruit can produce severe dermatitis in some people, much like "poison ivy," to which it is distantly related.

**Mago** is a large, spreading tree up to 25 m in height, often forming a massive trunk. The simple, alternately arranged leaves have a lanceolate blade 10—30 cm long. The tiny white to pink flowers are numerous in branching panicles. The fruit, red to yellow at maturity, is an obovoid drupe up to 10 cm or more long, with a pungent orange pulp and a single flattened, fibrous seed within.

**USES:** In one of the most common folk medicines for infants, an infusion of the scraped bark is given as a potion for treating mouth infections (*pala gutu*).

## MAKERITA
## (LĀ'AU SAUGA)

**SCIENTIFIC NAME:** *Tagetes erecta* L.
**FAMILY:** Asteraceae or Compositae (sunflower family)
**ENGLISH NAME:** African marigold

*Tagetes erecta* is native to Mexico, but is now widely distributed in the tropics as an ornamental flower. It is a European introduction to Samoa, where it is common in flower gardens around houses. Both Samoan names also apply to different plants (**makerita** to *Zinnia elegans* and **lā'au sauga** to *Ocimum* spp.), so there is some confusion about identity when the two names are used.

**Makerita** is an erect annual herb mostly 30—60 cm in height. The strongly scented leaves, up to 12 cm long, are oppositely arranged on the lower stem, alternate on the upper stem, and deeply pinnately lobed. The solitary heads, which are borne on a long stalk that is widened near the top, are 5—7 cm wide with numerous showy orange to yellow ray florets. The fruit is an achene with several unequal scales 3—10 mm long at the top.

**USES:** The juice from the rolled and crushed leaves is sometimes dripped onto fresh wounds (*manu'a* and *lavea*).

## MAMALA

**SCIENTIFIC NAME:** *Omalanthus nutans* (Forst. f.) Guillemin
**FAMILY:** Euphorbiaceae (spurge family)
**ENGLISH NAME:** none

*Omalanthus nutans* is native from New Caledonia to Tahiti, and is found on most of the high islands in this range. It is a common tree in abandoned plantations and secondary scrub in Samoa, sometimes dominating these types of vegetation, mostly in the lowlands but sometimes at up to over 1000 m elevation. The only significant uses for this plant are medicinal. In previous times it was apparently called **fogāmamala** or **fanuamamala**, but nowadays these are rarely used and the plant is simply called **mamala**. The spelling of "*Homalanthus*" by some authors is apparently incorrect (see A.C. Smith 1981: p. 558).

**Mamala** is a small tree up to 10 m in height, with milky sap. The simple, alternately arranged leaves have a triangular to broadly ovate blade 3—15 cm long, with a somewhat waxy surface darker on the upper than the lower side. The flowers are in separate male and female inflorescences. The tiny yellowish male flowers are in long, narrow racemes. The female flowers are solitary, with two style lobes. The flattened-ovoid fruit is red at maturity and is borne on a long stalk.

**USES:** The tree finds only occasional use in Samoa, although in former times the leaves were often used to bandage circumcision wounds. An infusion of the crushed leaves or scraped bark is sometimes taken as a potion for treating urinary tract problems (*tulitā*) and as a purgative to clean the digestive tract. Cox and Balick (1994) noted the presence of a compound called prostratin in this plant, which has some potential in treating AIDS, but the plant is rarely used in Samoa for treating for viral infections, especially not for yellow fever, which does not occur there.

## MASAME

**SCIENTIFIC NAME:** *Glochidion ramiflorum* Forst.
**FAMILY:** Euphorbiaceae (spurge family)
**ENGLISH NAME:** none

*Glochidion ramiflorum* is native from Vanuatu (New Hebrides) to the Marquesas Islands, but there is some difference of opinion as to the exact range of this species, and whether or not the populations on some islands within this range should be recognized as separate species. In Samoa, it occurs in primary and secondary forest at all elevations, but most frequently in disturbed vegetation and on lowland lava flows. It is occasional to common, but is rarely a dominant species.

**Masame** is a small to medium-sized tree up to 10 m or more in height. The simple, alternately arranged leaves have a lanceolate to elliptic blade mostly 4—15 cm long. The tiny, unisexual, yellow flowers are in axillary clusters. The fruit is a wheel-like capsule 6—12 mm in diameter, green at maturity and splitting into several sections, each containing two red seeds.

**USES:** An infusion of the scraped bark or crushed leaves is commonly taken as a potion, or the juice from the chewed leaves is dripped into an infant's mouth for treating mouth infections (*pala gutu* and *pala fefie*), a use also reported from Tonga. Less commonly, an infusion of the crushed leaves is boiled and taken as a potion for treating bruises (*uno'o*).

# MATALAFI

**SCIENTIFIC NAME:** *Psychotria insularum* A. Gray
**FAMILY:** Rubiaceae (coffee family)
**ENGLISH NAME:** none

*Psychotria insularum* is native to much of western Polynesia, but is most frequent in Samoa, where it is a common tree in the understory of lowland and montane forest up to over 1000 m elevation. The genus *Psychotria* is the largest in Samoa, with 20 species, nearly all of them found only in Samoa. Many of these would also be called **matalafi**, but they are all much less common and are probably not used medicinally. Some healers distinguish a **matalafi tane** (male) and a **matalafi fafine** (female) on the basis of leaf differences.

**Matalafi** is a shrub or small tree mostly less than 2 m in height. The simple, oppositely arranged leaves have an elliptic blade 8—20 cm long. The flowers are arranged in axillary or terminal clusters. The white, tubular to bell-shaped, 5-lobed corolla is 4—8 mm long. The fruit is a glossy red, subglobose berry up to 1 cm long, containing two large seeds stuck together in the center.

**USES:** This is one of the most frequently used medicinal plants in Samoa, and is believed to be the one most effective in treating supernaturally induced ailments. It is also used by healers who do not believe in ghosts, but who probably view it as a cure-all. An infusion of the crushed leaves or scraped bark is commonly taken as a potion or is rubbed onto the skin for treating various kinds of inflammation (*mūmū*) and for supernaturally induced ailments such as *sāua* and possession (*ma'i aitu*). Less commonly, an infusion of the crushed leaves is applied to infected wounds (*fāoailetā*, *'oloā*, and *manu'a 'ona*), and is taken as a potion for treating swellings (*fula*) and various body aches.

# MATI

**SCIENTIFIC NAME:** *Ficus tinctoria* Forst. f.
**FAMILY:** Moraceae (mulberry family)
**ENGLISH NAME:** dyer's fig

*Ficus tinctoria* is native from India eastward as far as Tahiti, and is found on most of the high islands of the tropical Pacific. It is common in open places in Samoa, such as on lava flows, and is also occasional as an understory tree in lowland forest. It may begin life as an epiphyte and eventually turn into a "strangler fig," but rarely does it become a banyan like *Ficus obliqua* (**aoa**). The fruits are edible, but there are no reports of them being eaten in Samoa.

**Mati** is a small tree mostly less than 4 m in height, with milky sap. The simple, alternately arranged leaves have a leathery, elliptic to oblong blade mostly 6—22 cm long. The tiny flowers are hidden within a globose structure called a syconium that matures into a subglobose, orange to red "fig" fruit 10—17 mm in diameter. A common related species (also called **mati** or **mati vao**, *Ficus scabra*) has broader leaves with a rough surface.

**USES:** The crushed leaves mixed with oil are sometimes applied to burns, and the sap collected from the inner bark is dripped into eyes for treating eye injuries (*mata pa'ia*) and pterygium (*moālili*).

## MAUTOFU

**SCIENTIFIC NAME:** *Sida rhombifolia* L.
**FAMILY:** Malvaceae (mallow family)
**ENGLISH NAME:** broom weed

    *Sida rhombifolia* is probably native to somewhere in the Old World tropics, but is now pantropic in distribution. It was an ancient introduction to Samoa, where it is a common weed of disturbed places such as plantations, roadsides, and pastures. Several other weedy shrubs are called by the same name and may also be used for medicine, but this species is usually described as the "small-leafed one."
    **Mautofu** is a much-branched shrub up to 1 m or more in height. The simple, alternately arranged leaves have a rhomboid to ovate blade 2—6 cm long with toothed margins. The flowers are solitary on long stalks from the leaf axils. The pale orange corolla is wheel-shaped, and consists of 5 petals with unequally bilobed tips. The many stamens are united into a tube surrounding the long, 5-lobed style. The fruit is a flattened-globose schizocarp that breaks at maturity into 9—12 segments.

**USES:** The crushed or chewed leaves are often applied to cuts (*lavea*), especially infected ones (such as *fāoailetā* and *'oloā sami*), and to boils (*sila'ilagi, ma'i sua*, and *mata o le i'a*). A similar use for treating boils is reported from the Philippines (de Padua *et al.* 1983).

## MAU'UTOGA

**SCIENTIFIC NAME:** *Commelina diffusa* Burm. f.
**FAMILY:** Commelinaceae (spiderwort family)
**ENGLISH NAMES:** commelina, day flower

    *Commelina diffusa* is native to tropical Asia, and by the European Era was distributed as far east as western Polynesia. It is probably an ancient introduction to Samoa, most likely from Tonga (judging by its name), and is now a common weed in disturbed places, especially in wet areas such as taro patches and along sunny stream banks.
    **Mau'utoga** is a sprawling, weak-stemmed herb with stems up to 75 cm long, rooting at the nodes. The simple, alternately arranged leaves have a lanceolate blade 3—10 cm long, with a petiole attached to a membranous sheath around the stem. The short, few-flowered inflorescences are enclosed within folded, ovate, green bracts 1.6—

2.5 cm long, opposite a leaf. The flowers are blue with 6 unequally shaped tepals. The fruit, which is also enclosed with the bracts, is a few-seeded capsule.

**USES:** The juice expressed from the crushed leaves is sometimes dripped onto cuts (*lavea*) to staunch the bleeding. A similar use is reported from Fiji (Smith 1979).

## MILO

**SCIENTIFIC NAME:** *Thespesia populnea* (L.) Sol. ex Corr.
**FAMILY:** Malvaceae (mallow family)
**ENGLISH NAMES:** milo, Pacific rosewood

*Thespesia populnea* is distributed from East Africa to eastern Polynesia, but may be an ancient introduction to Polynesia, at least to the eastern part. It is probably native to Samoa, where it is occasional to common in littoral forest and coastal villages, but is rarely found inland. The hard, durable timber is esteemed because it is resistant to decay in water and takes a good polish.

**Milo** is a small to medium-sized tree up to 12 m in height. The simple, alternately arranged leaves have a glossy, heart-shaped blade 8—16 cm long. The flowers, which are solitary in the leaf axils, have a showy corolla with five petals 4—8 cm long, yellow with purple at the base. The numerous stamens are united into a column surrounding the long style. The fruit is a brown, flattened-globose, non-splitting capsule 2—3 cm across, which at maturity contains a sticky yellow sap and about 10 hairy seeds.

**USES:** An infusion of the scraped bark is often taken as a potion for treating mouth infections (*pala fefie* and *pala gutu*), a use also reported from Tonga. Less commonly, the infusion is taken as a purgative for treating stomachache (*manava tīgā*), worms (*'anufe*), and relapse sickness (*failele gau*).

## MOEGĀLŌ

**SCIENTIFIC NAME:** *Cymbopogon citratus* (DC. ex Nees) Stapf
**FAMILY:** Poaceae or Gramineae (grass family)
**ENGLISH NAME:** lemon grass

*Cymbopogon citratus* is native to the Old World tropics, but is now widely cultivated throughout the tropics and subtropics. It is a European introduction to Samoa, where it is occasional in cultivation around houses. The identification of this species is tentative, since it has not been noted to produce flowers in Samoa.

**Moegālō** is a clump-forming grass up to 1.5 m in height, but usually much shorter. The lemon-scented, linear blades are up to 1 m long and mostly 5—20 mm wide. The ligule is truncate and up to 2 mm long. The spikelets are in dissimilar pairs, one sessile, one stalked, but are not known to form in Samoa.

**USES:** In one of the most common folk remedies for infants (also applied by healers), the juice from the crushed or chewed roots or leaves is dripped onto mouth sores (*gutu malū*) and mouth infections (*pala gutu*). Sometimes the leaves are crushed and made into an infusion instead. A similar use is reported from Tonga.

## MOLI ʻAINA

**SCIENTIFIC NAME:** *Citrus sinensis* (L.) Osbeck
**FAMILY:** Rutaceae (citrus family)
**ENGLISH NAMES:** orange, sweet orange

*Citrus sinensis* is probably native to Southeast Asia, but reached the Mediterranean in the late 15th century, and from there was introduced throughout the tropical and warm-temperate regions of the world, including all the high islands of Polynesia. It is occasional in cultivation in villages and plantations in Samoa, where it is grown for its edible fruit. Other species of oranges are sometimes used interchangeably in Samoan medicine.

**Moli ʻaina** is a medium-sized tree up to 10 m in height, with or without axillary spines. The simple, alternately arranged leaves have a glossy, ovate to elliptic blade mostly 5—12 cm long, with a narrowly winged petiole. The flowers are solitary or are few in axillary racemes. The white, fragrant corolla has five oblong petals 1.2—2.5 cm long, and 20—25 stamens. The fruit is an orange, sweet-pulped, globose berry mostly 5—10 cm in diameter, with a rind about 5 mm thick.

**USES:** An infusion of the scraped bark is occasionally taken as a potion for treating postpartum sickness (*failele gau*), serious flu (*fulū gau*), and internal injuries (*gau*).

## MOSOʻOI

**SCIENTIFIC NAME:** *Cananga odorata* (Lam.) Hook. f. & Thoms.
**FAMILY:** Annonaceae (soursop family)
**ENGLISH NAMES:** ilangilang, perfume tree

*Cananga odorata* is native to Southeast Asia, possibly originally to the Philippines, but is now widely cultivated in the tropics. It was probably an ancient introduction to Samoa and the rest of western Polynesia, but did not reach Tahiti and the rest of eastern Polynesia until the European Era. The tree is common in secondary forest and clearings, but usually does not persist in mature forest. It is valued mostly for its showy, fragrant flowers used to make leis and scented coconut oil. The fragrance arises from an essential oil, which in the Philippines is distilled from the flowers and used to make perfume.

**Mosoʻoi** is a tall, narrow tree up to 20 m in height, with spirally arranged branches. The simple, alternately arranged leaves are in one plane, with an oblong to elliptic blade up to 25 cm long. The flowers are arranged in clusters and have six fragrant, yellowish green, linear-lanceolate petals 4—9 cm long. The fruit is a black, fleshy berry 1—2 cm long, containing 6—12 seeds.

USES: An infusion of the scraped bark is often taken as a potion for treating various ailments, such as postpartum sickness (*failele gau*), constipation (*manava mamau*), stomachache (*manava tīgā*), and an internal pain called *toʻala*. A similar use, as a purgative, is reported from Tonga. Less commonly, the same infusion is used for treating mouth infections (*pala gutu*) and coughs (*tale*). A boiled infusion of the leaves and/or flowers is sometimes given as a steam bath or bath as a closing ceremony after treatment, probably as a "ghost medicine."

## NAMULEGA

**SCIENTIFIC NAME:** *Vitex trifolia* L.
**FAMILY:** Verbenaceae (verbena family)
**ENGLISH NAME:** none

*Vitex trifolia* is distributed from East Africa to the Marquesas Islands, and is native to Samoa, where it is uncommon near the sea in coastal thickets and littoral scrub vegetation, but is sometimes cultivated in villages. Few uses, other than medicinal ones, have been reported for this plant, although the leaves may have been burned in former times to repel mosquitoes at night.

**Namulega** is a shrub mostly l.5—5 m in height. The oppositely arranged, palmately compound leaves are divided into 3—5 elliptic to lanceolate leaflets 1—10 cm long, with the lower leaf surface gray-green and the upper dark green. The flowers are in narrow, short-branched, terminal panicles. The lavender, five-lobed corolla is 5—7 mm long with a distinct upper and lower "lip." The fruit is a hard, green, globose, 4-seeded capsule about 5 mm in diameter, surrounded by a persistent, saucer-shaped calyx.

USES: An infusion of the crushed leaves is often taken as a potion for treating respiratory difficulties (*sela*). An infusion of the leaves has been reported my many sources (Krämer 1902—1903, Hunt 1923, Setchell 1924, Christophersen 1935, McCuddin 1974, and Uhe 1974) for treating fever by inducing sweating, but this appears to be uncommon now.

## N I U

**SCIENTIFIC NAME:** *Cocos nucifera* L.
**FAMILY:** Arecaceae or Palmae (palm family)
**ENGLISH NAME:** coconut

The coconut is native to somewhere in the Old World tropics, but spread naturally and by introduction throughout the area. At the time of Columbus' arrival in the New World, the coconut had not yet reached the Caribbean. It is probably native to Samoa, but the most common varieties were introduced by the ancient Samoans and others in more recent times. The coconut is the most useful tree in Samoa, and is a source of food, drink, thatch, and timber, among other uses.

**Niu** is a tall palm tree up to 20 m or more in height, but usually much less. The large, spirally arranged leaves are up to 6 m or more in length, and are pinnately divided into numerous strap-shaped segments. The separate male and female flowers are in axillary panicles. The male flowers have 3 yellow petals and 6 stamens. The ovoid coconut is up to 20—30 cm long, and is composed of a thick fibrous husk, a hard shell, and a single seed with the copra lining the interior, and water (coconut water) filling the cavity when it is young.

**USES:** The juice squeezed from the husk of a coconut that has not fallen to the ground is commonly dripped into the mouth of a newborn baby to treat an ailment called *la'ofia* or *lanuia*, which is believed to be caused by the fetus swallowing the meconium in the amniotic fluid before birth. Less commonly, it is given to infants to treat childhood ailments known as *ila fale* and *ila mea*.

## NONU
## (NONU TOGĪANONU)

**SCIENTIFIC NAME:** *Morinda citrifolia* L.
**FAMILY:** Rubiaceae (coffee family)
**ENGLISH NAME:** Indian mulberry

*Morinda citrifolia* is distributed from India to Hawai'i, but was originally native only to Southeast Asia, possibly only to the islands of Indonesia, and was probably carried by ancient seafarers over most of its current range. It occurs mostly in open coastal areas and lowland forests in Samoa, in disturbed places as a weed, and is sometimes casually cultivated in villages. The Indian mulberry was a valuable dye plant: a red dye was made from the bark, and more commonly, a yellow dye from the roots. The fruit, although unpleasant-tasting and foul-smelling when ripe, serves as food for pigs, and in times of famine, for humans as well. The plant was also one of the most widely used medicinal plants of ancient Polynesia. Some healers recognize a **nonu tane** (male) and **nonu fafine** (female) based upon differences in the leaves.
**Nonu** is a glabrous shrub or small tree up to 8 m in height, with four-angled stems and large, rounded stipules between the petiole bases. The simple, oppositely arranged leaves have an elliptic to ovate blade 15—35 cm long. The flowers are in a stalked, subglobose head arising from an upper node opposite an unpaired leaf. The white, tubular corolla is about 15 mm long, with five spreading lobes. The large, fleshy, translucent to gray, ovoid to elliptic fruit is up to 12 cm or more long, with a lumpy surface covered by many polygonal sections formed by the fusion of the ovaries.

**USES:** This is probably the most widely and commonly used medicinal plant in Polynesia, and is part of many medicinal treatments in Samoa. The odor of the plant is thought, by those who believe in supernaturally induced ailments, to repel ghosts. In a common folk remedy, a leaf is snapped near a sty (*matafā*) and a flower is touched to it (right hand to left eye, or left hand to right eye). A similar practice is reported from Tonga. The leaves (or an infusion of the young leaves) are often massaged onto body aches and various kinds of inflammation (*mūmū*). The same medicine is sometimes massaged onto boils (*ma'i sua*) and infected wounds (*'oloā*), as is done in Tonga, and to swellings (*fula*). An infusion of the small crushed fruits is occasionally taken as a potion for treating mouth infections (*pala fefie*), and less commonly for urinary tract problems (*tulitā*), respiratory difficulty (*sela*), and fever with jaundice (*fiva samasama*).

## NONU FI'AFI'A
## (NONU 'AI)

**SCIENTIFIC NAME:** *Syzygium malaccense* (L.) Merr. & Perry
**FAMILY:** Myrtaceae (myrtle family)
**ENGLISH NAMES:** Malay apple, mountain apple

*Syzygium malaccense* is distributed from India and Asia to eastern Polynesia, but is probably native only to Malaysia, and was carried throughout Polynesia by ancient voyagers. In Samoa, it is uncommon in villages, lowland secondary forests, and cultivated valleys. The tree is esteemed for its edible fruit, but is also widely known for its medicinal uses, which are mostly related to the astringent properties of the bark.

**Nonu fi'afi'a** is a medium-sized tree 15 m or more in height. The simple, oppositely arranged leaves have a glossy, ovate to oblong blade mostly 10—30 cm long. The flowers are borne in short, few-flowered cymes on the trunks of older branches. The calyx is top-shaped with four rounded lobes, and the four red petals fall early to expose the numerous showy red stamens 1—2 cm long. The fleshy, glossy, red to white, obovoid fruit is mostly 3—7 cm long, and contains a single large seed.

**USES:** To treat mouth infections (*pala, gutu malū*, and *eaea*), an infusion of the crushed leaves or scraped bark is very commonly taken as a potion, the leaves are chewed and the juice swallowed, or the leaf juice is dripped into the mouth of an infant. Similar treatment is reported from the Cook Islands (Whistler 1985) and Tonga.

## 'O'A

**SCIENTIFIC NAME:** *Bischofia javanica* Bl.
**FAMILY:** Euphorbiaceae (spurge family)
**ENGLISH NAME:** none

*Bischofia javanica* is distributed from India eastward to the Cook Islands, but is possibly an ancient introduction in the eastern part of its range. In Samoa, it is occasional in secondary forest and plantations, but is more common in montane and cloud forest, where it appears to be native. The tree has long been used as a dye plant: the scraped bark is squeezed and the sap expressed from it is rubbed onto tapa cloth with a piece of cloth to give tapa its characteristic red-brown color.

**'O'a** is a large, spreading tree up to 20 m or more in height. The alternately arranged, trifoliate leaves have ovate leaflets mostly 4—12 cm long. The small, inconspicuous flowers are unisexual on separate male and female trees, and lack petals.

The male flowers have five stamens, the female flowers a three-celled ovary bearing three stigmas. The fruit is a small, subglobose berry 4—8 mm in diameter, brown to purple at maturity, with the persistent stigmas on top.

**USES:** An infusion of the scraped bark is commonly taken as a potion for treating mouth infections or sores (*gutu malū* and *pala gutu*). Sometimes, sap from the scraped bark is rubbed onto the sores, or an infusion of the crushed leaves is taken as a potion. Similar treatment is reported from Tonga. Less commonly, juice from the chewed leaves or an infusion of the crushed leaves is dripped into the eye to treat eye injuries (*mata pa'ia*), blurry vision (*mata puaoa*), and eyelid infections (*fuafua lili'i*).

## 'OFE
### ('OFE SAMOA)

**SCIENTIFIC NAME:** *Schizostachyum glaucifolium* (Rupr.) Munro
**FAMILY:** Poaceae or Gramineae (grass family)
**ENGLISH NAME:** Polynesian bamboo

The Polynesian bamboo is probably native to Fiji, but was carried in ancient times eastward across the Pacific as far as Hawai'i, and is found on most of the high islands of this region. It is occasional in Samoa in plantations, and sometimes in thickets in the forest, where it is probably a relict of former cultivation. It has largely been replaced in common usage by the introduced bamboo, *Bambusa vulgaris* Schrad. ex Wendl., called **'ofe Fiti**. This latter species is often used medicinally in the same ways as the Samoan **'ofe**.

**'Ofe** is a large bamboo up to 15 m in height, with green, jointed stems 3.5—6 cm in diameter. Slender branches 60—120 cm long form at the nodes. At the base of the leaf surrounding the stem is a large deciduous sheath densely covered with hairs, bearing a narrow bent-back tip. The leaves are linear-lanceolate, parallel veined, and up to 30 cm long. The flowers are in 1-flowered spikelets borne in long narrow spikes, but rarely occur in Samoa; when they do, the whole population flowers at once.

**USES:** In one of the most common Samoan folk remedies, a mixture of the ashes from the burned leaves and coconut oil is applied to burns (*mū*).

## OGOOGO
### (OGOOGO TOTO)

**SCIENTIFIC NAME:** *Laportea interrupta* (L.) Chew
**FAMILY:** Urticaceae (nettle family)
**ENGLISH NAME:** island nettle

*Laportea interrupta*, which until recently was called *Fleurya interrupta*, is probably native to somewhere in Southeast Asia, but is now widespread as a weed from Africa eastward to Hawai'i (where it is apparently no longer found). It was an ancient introduction to Samoa, where it is now uncommon as a weed of disturbed places, especially around houses in villages. There has been much confusion about the identity of **ogoogo**, since two species are distinguished, **ogoogo tea** or **ogoogo sina** (*Acalypha lanceolata*) and **ogoogo toto** (*Laportea interrupta*), based on the color of the stems.

Ogoogo is an herb up to 70 cm in height. The simple, alternately arranged leaves have an ovate blade mostly 3—8 cm long, with the margins toothed and the surfaces bearing mildly stinging hairs. The tiny green, inconspicuous, unisexual flowers lack petals and are borne in axillary panicles. The tiny green fruit contains a single ovoid seed.

**USES:** An infusion of the crushed or scraped stems is occasionally given to infants as a potion for treating *la'ofia* or *lanuia*, which is believed to be caused by the fetus swallowing the meconium in the amniotic fluid before birth. Less commonly, the leaves are chewed and dripped into red itchy eyes (*ogoogo*) of an infant.

## OGOOGO TEA
### (OGOOGO SINA, OGOOGO PA'EPA'E)

**SCIENTIFIC NAME:** *Acalypha lanceolata* Willd.
**FAMILY:** Euphorbiaceae (spurge family)
**ENGLISH NAME:** none

*Acalypha lanceolata* is native to somewhere in the Old World tropics. It was a European introduction to Samoa, where it is occasional as a weed of disturbed places in villages and plantations. It is easily confused with **ogoogo toto**, but healers distinguish it by its green rather than red stems, but this difference is sometimes unclear.

Ogoogo tea is an erect herb up to 1 m in height. The simple, alternately arranged leaves have an ovate blade 1—8 cm long, with coarsely toothed margins and densely pubescent surfaces. The many tiny green, apetalous (lacking petals), unisexual flowers are arranged on axillary spikes 5—30 mm long, with the female ones borne in a sheathing bract. The tiny green, 3-lobed fruit splits into three 1-seeded segments at maturity.

**USES:** The juice from the crushed leaves and/or stems is occasionally dripped into swollen, red, or sore eyes (*ma'i mata*).

## PATE

**SCIENTIFIC NAME:** *Coleus scutellarioides* (L.) Benth.
**FAMILY:** Lamiaceae or Labiatae (mint family)
**ENGLISH NAMES:** coleus, variegated coleus

Variegated coleus is native to tropical Asia, but is now cultivated throughout the tropics for its attractive, colorful foliage. It is a European introduction to Samoa, where it is commonly grown around houses, and is also found in plantations, often in hedges. A small wasp that preys on the taro-damaging larva of a moth feeds on the nectar of this plant, which may be the reason it is so frequently planted by farmers around their taro patches. It was formerly known as *Coleus blumei*, and the name used by some current authors is *Solenostemon scutellarioides* (L.) Codd.

Pate is an erect herb up to 1 m in height, with square stems. The simple, oppositely arranged leaves have a variegated (often with red or purple), ovate blade 4—15 cm long with crenate (rounded teeth) margins. The flowers are borne in clusters on terminal racemes mostly 5—10 cm long. The blue to purple, 2-lipped corolla is 8—13 mm long. The fruit is composed of 4 tiny nutlets that split apart at maturity.

USES: The leaves are commonly rubbed in the hands and the juice expressed from them is dripped onto skin sores (*po'u* or *papala*).

## POLO FEŪ

SCIENTIFIC NAME: *Capsicum frutescens* L.
FAMILY: Solanaceae (nightshade family)
ENGLISH NAMES: chili pepper, red pepper

*Capsicum frutescens* is native to tropical America, but is now widely distributed throughout the warm regions of the world. It was an early European introduction to Samoa, where it is grown in villages for its spicy fruit, but escapes from cultivation and becomes somewhat weedy in disturbed places. The fruit contains a powerful local stimulant known as capsaicin, which, when applied to the skin, produces a sensation of warmth without reddening; at higher concentrations, an intolerable burning sensation is produced, without blistering.

Polo feū is a woody, branching shrub up to 2 m in height. The simple, alternately arranged leaves have an ovate to lanceolate blade 4—12 cm long. The flowers are solitary or 2—3 in the leaf axils, reflexed atop a stalk mostly 1—2 cm long. The greenish white, wheel-shaped corolla is about 1 cm in diameter, with five yellow stamens. The fruit is a red, ovoid to ellipsoid berry 2—3 cm long, with a very pungent taste.

USES: In a common folk medicine, the leaves are chewed, crushed, or heated over a fire and applied to boils (*ma'i sua* and *sila'ilagi*) and infected wounds (*'oloā*). A similar use is reported from the Cook Islands (Whistler 1985) and Tonga, and in Samoa probably originally involved *Solanum americanum* Mill., which seems to have been virtually forgotten. Less commonly, an infusion of the crushed leaves and/or fruits is taken as a potion for treating various pains (*tīgā*), respiratory difficulties (*sela*), and coughs (*tale*).

## PU'A

SCIENTIFIC NAME: *Hernandia nymphaeifolia* (Presl) Kub.
FAMILY: Hernandiaceae (hernandia family)
ENGLISH NAME: Chinese-lantern tree

*Hernandia nymphaeifolia* ranges from tropical East Africa eastward as far as Tahiti, and is found on most of the high islands and some atolls in the tropical Pacific. It is a common tree in the littoral forest of Samoa, mostly on sandy beaches. On rocky shores it is usually replaced by **futu**, *Barringtonia asiatica*. The light wood is favored for making outrigger canoes, and the seeds are used as marbles. Until recently this tree was known as *Hernandia peltata*.

**Pu'a** is a large tree up to 20 m in height, often with a massive trunk. The simple, alternately arranged leaves have the petiole attached to the lower surface (rather than to the edge), and have a leathery, heart-shaped blade 7—20 cm long. The white, unisexual flowers are borne in clusters of 3 in axillary cymes on a long stalk. The male flowers have 3 sepals, petals, and stamens, the female flowers have 4 sepals, 4 petals, and a single ovary. The fruit is a black, ellipsoid drupe 15—23 mm long, surrounded by a yellowish white lanternlike structure open at the top.

**USES:** An infusion of the crushed bark is occasionally taken as a potion for treating postpartum sickness (*failele gau*).

## PUA FITI
## (PUA)

**SCIENTIFIC NAME:** *Plumeria rubra* L.
**FAMILY:** Apocynaceae (dogbane family)
**ENGLISH NAMES:** plumeria, frangipani

Frangipani is native to tropical America from Mexico to Panama, but is now cultivated throughout the tropics for its showy fragrant flowers. It was an early European introduction to Samoa, presumably from Fiji (hence the name **pua Fiti**), and is widely cultivated in villages for its flowers.

**Pua Fiti** is a freely branched tree up to 6 m or more in height, with thick stems and a copious milky sap. The leaves are spirally arranged at the ends of the branches, with an elliptic blade mostly 20—35 cm long with an acute tip. The flowers are arranged in large, terminal or lateral inflorescences. The 5-lobed, funnel-shaped corolla is about 5 cm in diameter and is white, pink, or yellow in color. The long, narrow fruits that contain many winged seeds are usually in spreading pairs, but are seldom seen in Samoa.

**USES:** The crushed or chopped leaves are often massaged onto the skin or applied as a plaster for treating various types of skin inflammation (*mūmū tatau* and *mūmū lele*).

## PUA SĀMOA
## (PUA, PUA TAHITI)

**SCIENTIFIC NAME:** *Gardenia taitensis* DC.
**FAMILY:** Rubiaceae (coffee family)
**ENGLISH NAME:** Tahitian gardenia

*Gardenia taitensis* ranges from Vanuatu (New Hebrides) to eastern Polynesia, but is probably native only in the western part of its distribution, and was an ancient introduction throughout Polynesia. In Samoa, it is mostly cultivated in villages for its fragrance and beauty, but is uncommon nowadays. It is also uncommon in sunny littoral areas, possibly as an escape from cultivation. Its flowers are fashioned into leis, are worn singly in the hair, and are added to coconut oil to impart their fragrance, but this is now infrequently done since the plant is so uncommon.

**Pua Sāmoa** is a shrub or small tree up to 6 m in height. The simple, oppositely arranged leaves have a glossy, obovate to broadly elliptic blade mostly 5—15 cm long. The showy white, fragrant flowers are solitary in the upper leaf axils, and have a sympetalous corolla with 6—8 spreading lobes 2—3.5 cm long. The fruit is a subglobose to ellipsoid, ribbed, many-seeded capsule 2.5—5 cm long, with a persistent necklike calyx on top, but cultivated plants rarely produce fruit.

**USES:** The crushed leaves or flowers are often massaged onto the skin or are made into an infusion taken as a potion for treating *mūmū tatau* and other kinds of inflammation. This may be related to a belief in the "ghost repelling" properties of this plant, as it is in Tonga. An infusion of the bark or leaves is sometimes used for treating supernaturally induced ailments (*ma'i aitu*).

## SALATO

**SCIENTIFIC NAME:** *Dendrocnide harveyi* (Seem.) Chew
**FAMILY:** Urticaceae (nettle family)
**ENGLISH NAME:** stinging nettle tree

*Dendrocnide harveyi* is native from Fiji to Niue, and in Samoa is occasional to locally common in secondary forest in the lowlands and montane region. Various parts of the plant are covered with stinging hairs. The soft wood is easily cut with a bush knife and is of no use.

**Salato** is a large tree with stinging hairs on many of its vegetative and flowering parts. The simple, alternately arranged, leaves have a broadly ovate blade 15—25 cm long, with coarsely dentate margins and the veins on the lower surface distinctly purple. The greenish, inconspicuous flowers are in terminal racemes. The fruits are small achenes embedded in the fleshy petiole.

**USES:** In a folk remedy known to those who frequent the forest, the sap from the bark is applied to stings from the plant (*mageso*) to alleviate the pain. The same folk remedy is used in Tonga.

## SEASEA

**SCIENTIFIC NAME:** *Syzygium corynocarpum* (A. Gray) C. Muell.
**FAMILY:** Myrtaceae (myrtle family)
**ENGLISH NAME:** none

*Syzygium corynocarpum* is probably native only to Fiji, but was an ancient introduction to western Polynesia. It is occasionally cultivated around houses in Samoa and is planted or perhaps escapes in plantations, but is almost never found in forest areas. The tree is valued mostly for its fragrant fruits that are used mainly for making leis. The fruits are also edible, but they are eaten mostly by children.

**Seasea** is a small to medium-sized tree mostly less than 5 m in height. The simple, oppositely arranged leaves have a glossy, lanceolate to oblanceolate blade 7—13 cm long. The flowers are borne in widely branching panicles. The top-shaped calyx is notched into four tiny lobes, and the four white petals are fused together into a cap that is shed early to expose the numerous white stamens. The fleshy, fragrant, 1-seeded, spindle-shaped to cylindrical fruit is 2.5—3.5 cm long, and is red to purple at maturity.

**USES:** A mixture of the crushed young leaves and coconut oil is commonly applied to skin sores (*po'u* and *papala*), and sometimes to various types of inflammation (*mūmū*), a use also reported from Tonga. An infusion of the scraped bark is sometimes taken as a potion for treating urinary tract problems (*tulitā*).

## SOI

**SCIENTIFIC NAME:** *Dioscorea bulbifera* L.
**FAMILY:** Dioscoreaceae (yam family)
**ENGLISH NAME:** bitter yam

The bitter yam is native to somewhere in the Old World tropics, but was spread in ancient times as far east as Hawai'i. It is an ancient introduction to Samoa, where it is a common weed of plantations and secondary forest. The underground and aerial tubers were formerly eaten in times of famine, but require much cooking to remove the bitter or poisonous compounds.

**Soi** is a high-climbing herbaceous vine arising from a large underground tuber. The simple, alternately arranged leaves have a heart-shaped blade 6—25 cm long, with 11—13 veins arising from the base. The flowers are in 2—6 hanging, simple or branched spikes. The three tiny white petals are 1—2 mm long. The papery, brown, oblong, 3-winged capsule is 2—3 cm long and contains several winged seeds.

**USES:** The crushed aerial tubers or leaves are sometimes applied to boils (*ma'i sua*), sometimes with coconut oil and at other times heated over a fire.

## TAGITAGI

**SCIENTIFIC NAME:** *Polyscias scutellaria* (Burm. f.) Fosb.
**FAMILY:** Araliaceae (panax family)
**ENGLISH NAME:** panax

*Polyscias scutellaria* is probably native to the Solomon Islands or Vanuatu (New Hebrides), but is now cultivated throughout the tropics for its showy foliage. It was an

90

early European introduction to Samoa, where it is cultivated in villages, often as a hedge plant. Several related species are all called by the same name, and some of them may also be used for Samoan medicines.

**Tagitagi** is a shrub up to 4 m in height. The alternately arranged leaves are simple or are divided into three or five broadly elliptic to round leaflets 8—22 cm long, with a wavy or lobed (and sometimes white) margin and surfaces green or variegated. The flowers, with 5 petals, are in small umbels arranged in large axillary or terminal panicles, but the plant rarely flowers in Samoa, and the 2-lobed fruits are not known to occur there.

**USES:** The crushed or chopped leaves are sometimes massaged or applied as a plaster to inflammations (*mūmū*) and swellings (*fula*).

## TĀIPOIPO
### (LAU MAFATIFATI, FUA PIPILO)

**SCIENTIFIC NAME:** *Geniostoma rupestre* Forst.
**FAMILY:** Loganiaceae (logania family)
**ENGLISH NAME:** none

*Geniostoma rupestre* is native from Melanesia to the Tuamotus, but some authors recognize instead numerous endemic species in the islands. In Samoa, it is occasional in coastal to montane forests, but is common on lowland lava flows of Savai'i. The leaves of the same or a related species in the Cook Islands are fragrant and are used in leis and for scenting coconut oil, but those of *Geniostoma rupestre* in Tonga are bad-smelling.

**Tāipoipo** is a shrub or small tree up to 6 m or more in height. The simple, oppositely arranged leaves have an ovate to elliptic blade 2—18 cm long. The flowers are in short, axillary inflorescences, with tiny white, 5-lobed corollas 2—5 mm long. The fruit is an ellipsoid capsule 5—9 mm long that splits open along two longitudinal seams to expose the numerous tiny red seeds.

**USES:** An infusion of the scraped bark or the chopped leaves is sometimes taken as a purgative for treating stomachache (*manava tīgā*), ulcers (*pala ga'au*), or worms ('*anufe*). A similar use is reported from Tonga.

## TALAFALU
### (TALAVALU)

**SCIENTIFIC NAME:** *Micromelum minutum* (Forst. f.) Seem.
**FAMILY:** Rutaceae (citrus family)
**ENGLISH NAME:** none

*Micromelum minutum* ranges from tropical Asia to western Polynesia, and appears to be native over this entire range. It is occasional as an understory tree in coastal, lowland, and secondary forests in Samoa, but relatively few people know its name nowadays.

**Talafalu** is a small tree up to 6 m in height. The alternately arranged, pinnately compound leaves are up to 50 cm long, with 7—12 alternate,unequally sided, ovate leaflets mostly 3—13 cm long. The flowers are in widely branching terminal and upper-axillary, many-flowered panicles. The fragrant corolla has five linear white petals up to 5 mm long. The fleshy, red, gland-dotted, ellipsoid fruit is up to l cm long.

**USES:** An infusion of the scraped bark is sometimes taken as a potion for treating stomach pain such as *osofā punimoa*. A similar use is reported from Tonga.

## TALIE

**SCIENTIFIC NAME:** *Terminalia catappa* L.
**FAMILY:** Combretaceae (tropical almond family)
**ENGLISH NAME:** tropical almond

*Terminalia catappa* ranges from tropical Asia to Polynesia, but has been introduced over much of this range, probably including Samoa. The tree is widely planted in coastal villages for its edible fruit, but since much effort is needed to extract the small kernel, it is eaten mostly by children or, in times of famine, by anyone. The tree is also valued for its fine wood that is employed for making houses, utensils, and gongs. In Savai'i, the common **talie** of the lowland forest is *Terminalia glabrata*, which is probably used medicinally in the same ways as the other species.

**Talie** is a large tree up to 30 m in height, with a broad trunk and thick, spreading branches. The simple, alternately arranged leaves are clustered at the ends of the branches and have a glossy, obovate blade mostly 8—30 cm long, which turns red before falling. The small, white five-lobed flowers 3—5 mm in diameter are numerous on spikes 8—23 cm long. The fruit is a red to purplish, winged, laterally compressed, ovoid drupe 2.5—6 cm long with a corky, fibrous husk surrounding the small, edible kernel.

**USES:** An infusion of the scraped bark is occasionally taken as a potion for treating mouth infections (*pala gutu* and *pala fefie*). A similar use is reported from Tonga.

## TEVE

**SCIENTIFIC NAME:** *Amorphophallus paeoniifolius* (Dennst.) Nicolson
**FAMILY:** Araceae (aroid family)
**ENGLISH NAME:** none

*Amorphophallus paeoniifolius* is native to tropical Asia or Indo-Malaysia, but was an ancient introduction eastward as far as Hawai'i. In Samoa, it is uncommon in secondary forest, plantations, and other disturbed places. In former times, the rhizome was eaten as a famine food, but it requires much cooking since it is very acrid.

**Teve** is a stemless herbaceous plant with an underground tuber up to 30 cm in diameter. The single leaf, which arises from the tuber after flowering, has a mottled petiole up to 1 m in height, and a large blade up to 1 m across, divided into 3 parts that are further pinnately lobed. The small, unisexual flowers are densely arranged together on a fleshy spadix arising from the ground, and surrounded by a large, foul-smelling, greenish-purple spathe.

**USES:** The juice from the stems is sometimes dripped into the eyes for treating eye ailments (*ma'i mata*) such as blurry vision (*mata 'avea*). Its use for conjunctivitis was first reported by Hunt (1923).

## TIPOLO
## (TIPOLO PATUPATU)

**SCIENTIFIC NAME:** *Citrus medica* L.
**FAMILY:** Rutaceae (citrus family)
**ENGLISH NAME:** citron

The citron is probably native to somewhere in the Middle East, but is now widespread in cultivation throughout the Old World tropics. It was introduced to Samoa sometime in the last century, and is occasional in cultivation. The juice from the fruits is used to make lemonade. The lime, *Citrus aurantiifolia* (Christm.) Swingle (**tipolo Sāmoa**), is sometimes used in the same ways in Samoan remedies.

**Tipolo** is a small tree up to 5 m in height, with short, sharp, axillary spines. The simple, alternately arranged, leathery leaves have a blade 7—18 cm long, with toothed margins, but with the petiole not expanded into a wing like many other citrus species. The fragrant flowers are arranged in short axillary racemes. The showy corolla has five white petals tinged pink on the outside, with 30—40 stamens. The oblong, lumpy, yellow fruit is 10—20 cm long, with a thick rind and a yellow, sour pulp.

**USES:** The juice from the chewed leaves is dripped into the mouth, or an infusion of the crushed leaves, often with those of *moegālō*, is occasionally taken as a potion for treating mouth infections (*pala gutu* and *pala fefie*). An infusion of the crushed leaves and the flowers of *pua Fiti* or *pua Sāmoa* is sometimes rubbed onto the skin for treating a kind of inflammation called *mūmū tatau*, in which the skin turns black.

## TOGO
## (TOGOTOGO, MOA)

**SCIENTIFIC NAME:** *Centella asiatica* (L.) Urb.
**FAMILY:** Apiaceae or Umbelliferae (carrot family)
**ENGLISH NAME:** Asiatic pennywort

*Centella asiatica* is native to tropical Asia, but is now widespread in the tropics and subtropics. It was a Polynesian or early European introduction to Samoa, where it is now a common weed of damp, sunny or shady places, such as forest clearings and pastures, and is often allowed to grow around houses for its medicinal uses.

**Togo** is a low, glabrous herb with erect leaves and prostrate stems that root at the nodes. The simple, alternately arranged leaves appear clustered at the nodes and have a broadly heart-shaped to kidney-shaped blade, often broader than wide, 2—7 cm across. The small, inconspicuous flowers are in short umbels borne in the leaf axils close to the ground. The fruit is a ribbed, subglobose capsule about 3 mm long, separating at maturity into two 1-seeded segments.

**USES:** This is one of the plants most commonly used for treating infants and children. An infusion of the crushed leaves, sometimes combined with those of other plants, is often given as a potion for treating childhood ailments called *ila mea, ila fale*, and *ila fa'a'autama*. The same medicine is often given as a potion or massaged onto the skin for treating various kinds of inflammation (*mūmū*). Less commonly, the crushed or chewed leaves, or their infusion, is rubbed onto the body for treating supernaturally induced ailments (*sāua* and *'oloā*), dripped into the eyes for eye ailments (*ma'i mata*), or applied to diaper rash (*mū*).

## TOLO

**SCIENTIFIC NAME:** *Saccharum officinarum* L.
**FAMILY:** Poaceae or Gramineae (grass family)
**ENGLISH NAME:** sugar cane

*Saccharum officinarum* is native to the Old World tropics, and was an ancient introduction as far east as Hawai'i. It is grown commercially in large fields in much of the tropics, but in Samoa is cultivated only in small patches in plantations and around houses, and is only used locally for the sugar in its stems and for the leaves employed for making thatch.

**Tolo** is a tall perennial grass up to 4 m or more in height, with thick, hard stems 3—5 cm in diameter, marked by conspicuous nodes. The lanceolate leaves are up to 1.5 m long and fall from the stems when they wither. The flowers are in large, dense, ovoid, terminal panicles with many fragile, jointed branches. The paired spikelets are similar and have long, silky hairs spreading from the base.

**USES:** The juice from the scraped stems, usually with cream from grated coconut, is very commonly given to a newborn baby with an ailment called *la'ofia* or *lanuia*, which is believed to be caused by the fetus swallowing the meconium in amniotic fluid before birth.

## U'A

**SCIENTIFIC NAME:** *Broussonetia papyrifera* (L.) Vent.
**FAMILY:** Moraceae (mulberry family)
**ENGLISH NAME:** paper mulberry

*Broussonetia papyrifera* is native to China and Japan, but was an ancient introduction as far east as Hawai'i. In Samoa, it is occasional in cultivation in plantations and around houses, but is seen much less frequently nowadays since the making of tapa cloth (which uses the inner stem bark of **u'a**) is no longer commonly practiced.

**U'a** is a shrub or small tree up to 8 m or more in height, with milky sap, densely hairy stems, and a fibrous bark that can be peeled off in long strips. The alternately arranged, simple leaves have an ovate blade up to 18 cm long, with a rough upper surface, velvety lower surface; margin entire to deeply lobed. It rarely flowers and never fruits in Samoa.

**USES:** An infusion of the crushed leaves is sometimes taken as a potion for treating stomach pains (*manava tīgā*) and ill-defined abdominal pains (*to'ala*).

## UFI
## (UFI VIOLĒ)

**SCIENTIFIC NAME:** *Boerhavia repens* L.
**FAMILY:** Nyctaginaceae (four-o'clock family)
**ENGLISH NAME:** none

*Boerhavia repens* ranges from Africa eastward to Hawai'i, but its native range is uncertain, since it appears to be mostly weedy in Polynesia. It is uncommon in disturbed places in Samoa, mostly in villages, particularly on rocky ground, and rarely (if ever) in plantations. Its Samoan name is confusing since it refers to the yam; however, the yam is not used in medicine, and is sometimes referred to as **ufi violē** or **ufi mūmū**, literally, "violet or red yam," referring to the color of the undersides of the leaves. In American Samoa, it is often called **a'atasi**, which elsewhere in Samoa is applied to *Rorippa sarmentosa*.

**Ufi** is a prostrate herb forming mats from a thick taproot. The simple, oppositely arranged leaves have a lanceolate to oblong blade 1—4 cm long, with the undersurface purple in color. The flowers are borne in long-stalked, axillary cymes. The corolla is missing, but the pink, bell-shaped calyx is 2—3 mm long. The tiny, sticky, club-shaped fruit is 3—4 mm long, and adheres to clothing.

**USES:** This plant is mostly restricted to treating ailments of children. An infusion of the crushed roots is commonly given as a potion for treating childhood ailments called *ila fale*, *ila mea*, and *ila fa'a'autama*.

## 'ULU

**SCIENTIFIC NAME:** *Artocarpus altilis* (Parkinson) Fosb.
**FAMILY:** Moraceae (mulberry family)
**ENGLISH NAME:** breadfruit tree

The breadfruit is native to Indo-Malaysia, possibly originally to the island of

Java, and was an ancient introduction eastward to Hawai'i. It is restricted to cultivation in Samoa, and trees occurring in forest areas are usually in abandoned plantations since most varieties are seedless. Its large, edible fruit is a staple food, and the durable and easily worked wood is used for building houses and outrigger canoes. The milky sap was commonly employed in caulking plank canoes, once widely used in Polynesia.

'**Ulu** is a large, attractive, round-topped tree up to 20 m or more in height, with a milky sap. The simple, alternately arranged leaves have a large, glossy, ovate to elliptic blade up to 60 cm long, usually with deeply toothed or lobed margins. The flowers are unisexual, with both occurring on the same tree. The tiny male flowers are in a densely packed cylindrical spike 7—25 cm long, while the female flowers are fused together into a globose head. The globose to ovoid fruit is up to 15 cm long, with the fused female flowers giving the surface a faceted appearance.

**USES:** The juice from the chewed or crushed petiole is occasionally dripped into eye injuries (*mata pa'ia*). The smoke from a hollow, burning breadfruit twig is sometimes blown onto the buttocks of an infant for treating childhood ailments collectively called *ila*, a use also reported from Tonga. An infusion from the scraped bark or root is sometimes taken as a potion for treating urinary tract problems (*tulitā*).

## USI
## (LAU USI)

**SCIENTIFIC NAME:** *Euodia hortensis* Forst.
**FAMILY:** Rutaceae (citrus family)
**ENGLISH NAME:** island musk

*Euodia hortensis* is widely distributed from Melanesia and Micronesia eastward as far as Niue, but is probably an ancient introduction to Polynesia. It grows around houses and occasionally in plantations in Samoa, and uncommonly in forests, where it is probably a relict of former cultivation. The shrub is well known as a medicinal plant whose usage probably dates to ancient times.

**Usi** is a shrub or small tree up to 6 m in height, but is usually much shorter. The fragrant, oppositely arranged, trifoliate leaves have three oblanceolate leaflets 7.5—15 cm long, or are sometimes simple with a linear-lanceolate blade 10—30 cm long. The flowers are in racemes or narrow panicles up to 25 cm long, borne in the upper leaf axils. The corolla has four tiny white petals 1—2 mm long. The fruit is divided into four subglobose, 1-seeded sections less than 5 mm long, green at maturity and splitting open to release their seeds.

**USES:** This is one of the best known plants in western Polynesia for treating supernaturally induced ailments. An infusion of the crushed or whole leaves, sometimes boiled, is commonly given as a bath, steam bath, or massage for treating "possession" (*ma'i aitu*) or as a closing procedure after treatment for other ailments to insure their efficacy. A similar use is reported from Tonga.

## VAO ĀPULUPULU

**SCIENTIFIC NAME:** *Chamaesyce hirta* (L.) Millsp.
**FAMILY:** Euphorbiaceae (spurge family)
**ENGLISH NAME:** garden spurge

*Chamaesyce hirta*, formerly known as *Euphorbia hirta*, is probably native to the somewhere in the Old World tropics, but is now pantropical in distribution. It is a European introduction to Samoa, where it is common in sunny, disturbed places such as roadsides, villages, and plantations. Children write something on their arms with the sap, which dries clear, then rub ashes across the sticky dry sap to make the words, or "tattoo," magically appear.

**Vao āpulupulu** is a small herb up to 60 cm in height with milky sap and hairy stems. The simple, oppositely arranged leaves have an oblong blade 1—4 cm long, with toothed margins. The greenish, inconspicuous flowers are clustered in "cyathia" arranged in globose cymes in the leaf axils. The fruit is a small green, globose schizocarp that splits into three 1-seeded segments at maturity.

**USES:** An infusion of the crushed plant is sometimes taken as a potion for treating stomachache (*manava tīgā*) and diarrhea (*manava tatā*). A similar use is reported from the Philippines (de Padua *et al.* 1981).

## VAO VAI

**SCIENTIFIC NAME:** *Peperomia pellucida* (L.) H.B.K.
**FAMILY:** Piperaceae (pepper family)
**ENGLISH NAME:** none

*Peperomia pellucida* is native to tropical America, but is now found as a weed throughout the tropics. It was first reported in Samoa in 1921, and is occasional to common in sunny, disturbed places such as on rocks in plantations and around houses. Its only reported uses are medicinal. Its Samoan name is not well known, but means "water weed."

**Vao vai** is a weak-stemmed, somewhat succulent herb 5—40 cm in height. The simple, alternately arranged have a heart-shaped blade 1—3.5 cm long, with several veins originating from the base. The tiny greenish flowers, lacking sepals or petals, are arranged in terminal spikes. The tiny green fruit, less than 1 mm in diameter, contains a single seed.

**USES:** The crushed plant is sometimes applied to boils (*ma'i sua*).

# VĪ

**SCIENTIFIC NAME:** *Spondias dulcis* Parkinson
**FAMILY:** Anacardiaceae (cashew family)
**ENGLISH NAME:** Otaheite apple, Polynesian plum

*Spondias dulcis* is native to the Malaysian area, but is now widely distributed in Southeast Asia, and was introduced by ancient seafarers into Polynesia as far east as the Marquesas Islands. It is widely cultivated in villages and plantations in Samoa and the rest of Polynesia, but is not reported to be naturalized. The tree is grown mainly for its edible, much esteemed fruit, but it is also valued for use in native medicines, some of which date to ancient times.

Vī is a large, spreading tree up to 20 m in height. The alternately arranged, odd-pinnately compound leaves have 5—15 pairs of lanceolate to elliptic leaflets mostly 4—10 cm long. The tiny flowers are numerous in large, branched panicles, and have a white corolla about 2 mm long. The yellowish, ovoid or obovoid, mango-like fruit is up to 8 cm long, with an edible outer, fibrous, fleshy portion enclosing the large seed.

**USES:** An infusion of the scraped bark is commonly taken as a potion for treating mouth infections (*pala gutu*), and less commonly for treating diarrhea (*manava tatā*), stomachache (*manava tīgā*), and ulcers (*pala ga'au*). The bark is used similarly in Tonga to treat digestive tract problems.

# VĪ VAO

**SCIENTIFIC NAME:** *Physalis angulata* L.
**FAMILY:** Solanaceae (nightshade family)
**ENGLISH NAME:** wild capegooseberry

*Physalis angulata*, formerly called *Physalis minima* by some authors, is native to tropical America, but appears to have been an ancient introduction to Polynesia. It is an occasional to common weed of disturbed places in Samoa, such as croplands and roadsides. The small edible fruits are eaten by children.

Vī vao is a large, much-branching herb up to 1 m in height. The simple, alternately arranged leaves have a lanceolate to ovate blade 2—12 cm long. The nodding flowers are solitary in the leaf axil. The broadly bell-shaped, shallowly 5-lobed corolla is yellow with darker spots at the base. The globose to ovoid berry is up to 1.5 cm in diameter, surrounded by the enlarged, inflated calyx.

**USES:** The leaves that have been crushed, chewed, or heated over a fire are sometimes applied to boils (*ma'i sua* and *sila'ilagi*), and less commonly, to wounds (*lavea*).

# LITERATURE CITED

Christophersen, E. 1935, 1938. Flowering plants of Samoa: I. Bishop Mus. Bull. 128: 1—221; II. 154:1—77.

Clement, D. C. 1974. Samoan concepts of mental illness and treatment. Ph.D. Thesis, Univ. of Calif., Irvine. 363 pp.

Cook, J. M. 1983. Samoan patterns in seeking health services. Hawaiian Med. Jour. 42 (6): 138—142.

Cox, P. A. 1990. "Samoan ethnopharmacology." *In* Economic and medicinal plant research. Vol. 4, Plants and traditional medicine. H. Wagner, H. Hikino, and N. R. Farnsworth (eds.), Academic Press, London.

Cox, P. A. 1991. "Polynesian herbal medicine." *In* Islands, Plants, and Polynesians. P. A. Cox & S. A. Banack (eds.), 147—168. Dioscorides Press, Portland, Oregon.

Cox, P. A. and M. J. Balick. 1994. The ethnobotanical approach to drug discovery. Scientific Amer. (June) p. 82—87.

Cox, P. A. *et al.* 1989. Pharmacological activity of the Samoan ethnopharmacopoeia. Econ. Bot. 43: 487—497.

Crawford, R. J. 1977. Missionary accounts of *fofō mo'omo'o*. Jour. Polynes. Soc. 86 (4): 531—534.

De Padua, L., G. C. Lugod, and J. V. Pancho. 1977, 1978, 1981, 1983. Handbook on Philippine medicinal plants. Univ. of Philippines, Los Baños. 4 vols.

Ella, S. 1892. "Samoa, etc.." *In* Articles on Polynesian and Melanesian ethnology. Australia Assoc. Adv. Sci. Rep. 4: 620—645.

Elmqvist, T. (ed.) 1993. The rain forest and the flying foxes. Fa'asao Savai'i, Salelologa, Savai'i. 96 pp.

Goodman, R. A. 1971. Some aitu beliefs of modern Samoans. Jour. Polynes. Soc. 80: 463—479.

Heath, T. 1840. The Navigator's or Samoa Islands: medicine and surgery. The Polynesian 17:65.

Heath, T. 1973. The diagnosis and treatment of disease in a rural village in Western Samoa. M.A. Thesis, Univ. Auckland.

Hunt, D. 1923. Samoan medicines and practices. U.S. Naval Med. Bull. 19 (2): 145—152.

Kinloch, P. J. 1980. Samoan health practices in Wellington. Management Serices and Research Unit, Occas. Pap. no. 12. Wellington, Dept. of Health. 38 pp.

Kinloch, P. J. 1985a. Talking health but doing sickness: studies in Samoan health. Victory Univ. Press, Wellington. 54 pp.

Kinloch, P. J. 1985b. "Midwives and midwifery in Western Samoa." *In* Healing practices in the South Pacific. Parsons, C. D. (ed.), 199—212. Inst. Polynes. Studies, La'ie, Hawai'i.

Krämer, A. 1902—1903. Die Samoa Inseln. E. Schwiezerbart, Stuttgart. 2 vols.

Macpherson, C. 1985. "Samoan medicine." *In* Healing practices in the South Pacific. Parsons, C. D. (ed.), 1—15. Inst. Polynes. Studies, La'ie, Hawai'i.

Macpherson, C., and L. Macpherson. 1990. Samoan medical belief and practice. Auckland Univ. Press. 272 pp.

Martin, J. [1817] 1981. Tonga Islands: William Mariner's account. Reprint. Vava'u Press, Tonga. 461 pp.

McCuddin, C. R. 1974. Samoan medicinal plants and their usage. Off. Comprehen. Health Planning, Depart. Med. Services, Govern. Am. Samoa. 35 pp. + 29 pp. Append.

Milner, G. B. 1966. Samoan dictionary. Oxford Univ. Press, London. 465 pp.

Moyle, R. M. 1974a. Samoan medical incantations. Jour. Polynes. Soc. 83 (2): 155—179.

Moyle, R. M. (ed.) 1974b. The Samoan journals of John Williams, 1830 and 1832. Australian Nat. Univ. Press, Canberra. 302 pp.

Neich, L. and R. Neich. 1974. Some modern Samoan beliefs concerning pregnancy, birth and infancy. Jour. Polynes. Soc. 83 (4):461—465.

Norton, T. R., M. L. Bristol, G. W. Read, O. A. Bushnell, M. Kashiwagi, C. M. Okinaga, and C. S. Oda. 1973. Pharmacological evaluation of medicinal plants from Western Samoa. Jour. Pharm. Sci. 62 (7): 1077—1082.

Powell, T. 1868. On various Samoan plants and their vernacular names. Jour. Bot. 6: 278—285; 342—347; 355—370.

Pratt, G. 1911. Pratt's grammar and dictionary of the Samoan language. Malua Printing Press, Apia. 512 pp.

Pritchard, W. T. 1866. Polynesian reminiscences. Chapman and Hall, London. 428 pp.

Schoeffel-Melaisea, P. 1978. Daughters of Sina. Ph.D. Thesis, Austr. Nat. Univer., Canberra.

Sesepasara, M. 1989. Traditional vs. Western medicine: to collaborate and integrate. M.S. thesis, University of Hawai'i. 24 pp.

Setchell, W. A. 1924. American Samoa. Carnegie Inst. Wash. 341 (Depart. of Marine Biol. 220): 1—275.

Smith, A. C. 1979—1991. Flora vitiensis nova: a new flora of Fiji. National Trop. Bot. Garden, Lawai, Kaua'i, Hawai'i. 5 vols.

Stair, J. B. 1897. Old Samoa, or flotsam and jetsam from the Pacific Ocean. The Religious Tract Society, London. 296 pp.

Turner, G. 1861. Nineteen years in Polynesia. J. Snow, London. 548 pp.

Uhe, G. 1974. Medicinal plants of Samoa: a preliminary survey of the use of plants for medicinal purposes in the Samoan Islands. Econ. Bot. 28: 1—39.

Whistler, W. A. 1984. Annotated list of Samoan plant names. Econ. Bot. 38 (4): 464—489.

Whistler, W. A. 1985. Traditional and herbal medicine in the Cook Islands. Jour. Ethnopharm. 13: 239—280.

Whistler, W. A. 1992a. Polynesian herbal medicine. National Trop. Bot. Garden, Lawai, Kaua'i, Hawai'i. 236 pp.

Whistler, W. A. 1992b. Tongan herbal medicine. Isle Botanica, Honolulu. 122 pp.

Whistler, W. A. 1992c. Flowers of the Pacific island seashore. Isle Botanica, Honolulu. 154 pp.

Whistler, W. A. 1995. Wayside plants of the islands. Isle Botanica, Honolulu. 202 pp.

Wilkes, C. [1845] 1970. Narrative of the United States Exploring Expedition. Reprint. Gregg Press, Upper Saddle River, New Jersey. 5 vols.

# GLOSSARY OF SAMOAN MEDICAL TERMS

The following glossary is based primarily on the author's interviews with Samoan healers, but some of the terminology of Krämer (1902—1903), Pratt (1911, but an earlier edition cited by Krämer), Milner (1966), Uhe (1974), McCuddin (1974), Macpherson and Macpherson (1990), and Cox (1990) are used.

This is not meant to be a complete dictionary of Samoan ailments, for several reasons. First, there is much variation in terminology among healers, and commonly accepted definitions are somewhat difficult to attain. Second, the terminology appears to be changing over time, since many of Pratt's illnesses and definitions recorded in the 19th century are not used today: of the numerous ailments discussed in Pratt, only a minority were validated during the interviews for this book. And third, many of the listed ailments cannot be equated to Western medical terminology.

Consequently, this is basically a reference list of the most common ailments recognized by Samoan healers today. Many of these names are not found in any of the Samoan dictionaries, but discussions of many of these ailments can be found in Macpherson and Macpherson and in McCuddin.

—A—

**'Anufe**— Intestinal worms, mostly of the genus *Ascaris*. Another type occasionally distinguished, hookworm, is called **'anufe matau**. Pratt noted the Tutuila name *unefe* for intestinal worms, and the Samoan name *'anufe* for worm.

**Asā**— Possibly a severe type of stomatitis, but the name is rarely used.

**Ate**— Liver, often used to refer to an illness of the liver.

**Ate fefete**— Literally, "swollen liver," but probably cirrhosis of the liver, which manifests itself by jaundice. The Macphersons noted that it is hardening of the liver associated with yellow jaundice.

**'Atiloto**— Usually a cold sore on the lips, but also applied to shingles (*Herpes zoster*), a viral disease that manifests itself as a line of blisters that follows the course of a nerve from the spinal cord. Pratt defined it as shingles, and **'atiloto** appears to be a cognate of the Niuean name for shingles. Milner defined it as erysipelas, which is caused by a hemolytic streptococcus bacteria. The Macphersons defined **'atiloto tatanu** as erysipelas.

**Aupā**— American Samoan name for **fiva samasama**; symptoms include yellow skin, face, and eyes. *Au* is a synonym for *ate*, liver. Some healers say the two are different, and that **aupā** is characterized by black skin.

—E—

**Ea**— Possibly indigestion causing diarrhea. The word may be a transliteration of "air," indicating that something is full of air, i.e., swollen or bloated.

**Eaea**— Thrush, a fungal disease (*Candida albicans*) infecting the mouth, lips, and throat. It sometimes causes fever. Called *kea* in Tonga.

**Eaea sā**— Perhaps another name for **eaea**, or thrush, characterized by white mouth, lips, and tongue. The Macphersons noted it as a congenital condition in which the interior of the mouth is white and covered with spreading pustules.

## —F—

**Fa'afaiavāina**— A type of **ma'i aitu** or **sāua** in which the ghost of a recently deceased person (usually a husband) returns to haunt his or her surviving spouse (usually the wife). See **fa'atausia**.

**Fa'aī a'ala**— Sore throat caused by inflammation of the mucous membrane of the pharynx.

**Fa'aifo'aluga**— An acute infection in the nose or sinus area, characterized by a runny nose, unpleasant-smelling sinuses, and sometimes shortness of breath.

**Fa'a'ī tigā**— Sore throat.

**Fa'alanu**— To chase ghosts away with the sprinkling of medicinal water.

**Fa'atausia**— A type of **ma'i aitu** or **sāua** in which the ghost of a recently deceased wife returns to haunt her surviving husband. See **fa'afaiavāina**.

**Fafine lē fananau**— Infertility of women.

**Failele gau**— Postpartum sickness of women, a commonly recognized illness. This condition may be diagnosed years after birth.

**Fāoailetā**— A type of boil or old infected wound, usually on the soles of the feet, that is difficult to cure. Also a general term for septicemia (blood poisoning).

**Fasia**— Another term for **ma'i fasia** or **ma'i aitu**, literally "struck."

**Fatafata vaivai**— An internal ailment, literally, "weak chest," identified by some healers as tuberculosis (**māmāpala**).

**Fe'e**— A kind of headache reported by Moyle. Literally, "octopus."

**Fe'efe'e**— Constipation characterized by black feces. Cox described it as pain in the back and stomach, with dark stools. Milner noted it as an inflammation from filariasis, and Pratt as elephantiasis.

**Fifi pa'ū**— Hernia, or traumatic injury to the testes and scrotum. The word is impolite and women do not use it when men are present. See **ma'i 'o tane**.

**Filogia**— A condition where blood is mixed with the feces, possibly caused by a bleeding ulcer; other definitions for this condition exist, including blood in the urine.

**Fiva**— Fever, a transliteration of the English word. Also called **vevela**.

**Fiva samasama**— Fever accompanied by jaundice, a yellowing of the skin and eyes usually caused by liver problems, such as hepatitis. Literally, "yellow fever." See also **aupā**.

**Fiva ta'ai**— A type of fever, literally, "trapped fever." It may be the same as **mūmū ta'ai**.

**Foe**— Sores on the scalp of a baby, possibly impetigo. Not noted in Milner or Pratt.

**Fuafua**— Pimple or abscess. Called *fuofua* in Tonga.

**Fuafua lili'i**— An infection on the upper eyelid, something like a sty.

**Fuafua momono**— Difficulty in swallowing, caused by inflammation of glands in the neck, or a furuncle in the nose or ear canal.

102

**Fula**— A general name for swelling, also as **fulafula**. Called by the same name in Tonga.

**Fula malō**— A type of hard swelling caused by a deep-seated abscess.

**Fula maua**— A deep abscess, causing a swelling.

**Fulū**— Flu, a transliteration of the English name.

**Fulū gau**— A serious or long-lasting flu.

**Fulu migi**— Muscle fatigue. Also defined by some as a stroke, or as a common cold with cramps and muscle fatigue.

—G—

**Ga'e**— Respiratory difficulty of children caused by some degree of obstruction of the air passage. The Macphersons equated it with **sela**, respiratory difficulties or asthma.

**Gasegase**— The polite word for "sickness." See **ma'i**.

**Gau**— Literally, a strain or break (e.g., a broken bone), but when following the name of another ailment it denotes a serious or recurring disease, such as **fulū gau**. Pratt and Milner defined **gau** as a relapse. See **failele gau**.

**Gau a'ano**— A serious internal injury, like a bruise, but lasting longer. Literally, "strained flesh." It may cause loss of weight, without other obvious signs of illness. This may correspond to *kafo* in Tonga.

**Gutu malū**— Stomatitis or sores inside the mouth, common in children and sometimes caused by burns from hot food or drink. Literally, "soft mouth."

**Gutu pala**— See **pala gutu**.

—I—

**I'atolo**— Multiple small boils that occur on the scalp. Spelled this way by Milner, but "*iatolo*" by Pratt. Called *kiatolo* in Tonga, where it is defined as "hard swellings on the neck" (Whistler 1992b).

**Ila**— A general term for a number of vaguely related diseases of infants and children, usually related to the area of the anus and genitals (i.e., area covered by diapers) or sometimes the mouth. These are not always distinct from **mūmū**. **Ila** also means birthmark or mole, but this is not what healers usually treat. Several kinds of **ila** are recognized, although their differences are not always clear. The most commonly recognized kinds are listed below.

**Ila fa'a'autama**— Ailment of infants characterized by a white mouth, loss of appetite, eyes and mouth partly open when sleeping, restless sleep, or continuous diarrhea. Some people attribute this to premature birth or to neglect by the mother.

**Ila fale**— Ailment of children who are tired and won't eat, but with no obvious physical manifestation. One source noted that the baby cries, won't eat, and sleeps with its bottom up. Some healers believe that it is caused by homesickness of the baby. Cox described it as an infection of the anus. This term is also used in Tonga.

**Ila mea**— Diaper rash (reddening of the buttocks and genital area). A disease of infants, according to Pratt, and an inflammation in the region of the anus caused by diarrhea, according to Milner. McCuddin noted it as a red spot that develops on the back of the head, possibly caused by an *aitu.*

**Ila sāua**— Type of ila, caused by spirits. See **sāua**.

**Ila toso**— Like **ila fale**, but the buttocks are extra red. Uhe defined it as "baby illness with fever, red eyes, loss of weight, and sometimes diarrhea." This **ila** is typically treated by dragging (*toso*) the baby on a mat around the healer.

**Isu mamafa**— Runny nose, as from a common cold or flu. Literally, "heavy nose."

—K—

**Kanesa**— Cancer, a transliteration of the English name.

—L—

**Lafa**— Ringworm, an introduced fungal disease of the skin. Called by the same name in Tonga.

**Lafitoga**— Warts found mostly on the eyelid. Defined by Pratt, who spelled it *lafetoga* (a spelling currently used by some people), as "a stye in the eye." Called *lefetona* in Tonga.

**Lālā vevela**— A type of rough skin caused by an infected rash that may cause intermittent fever.

**Lanuia**— Another name for **la'ofia**.

**Laoa**— A fishbone caught in the throat.

**La'ofia**— Ailment of newborn babies, characterized by crying, runny nose, and a gurgling, labored breathing. It is caused by fetal ingestion of the meconium ("meconium aspiration"), the waste product excrete prematurely into the amniotic fluid. Healers believe that if the infant is not treated, it will be adversely affected later in life. Also called **lanuia**.

**Lavea**— A cut or wound, often used interchangeably with **manu'a**. Called by the same name in Tonga.

**Lepela**— Leprosy, now virtually eliminated from Samoa.

**Lima gau**— A broken hand or arm. Also called **gau 'o le lima**.

**Līmonia**— As "*fiva limōnia*" in Milner, pneumonia. See **nīmonia**.

**Lipi**— Enlarged, infected glands in the neck, often causing some difficulty in swallowing and excessive salivation. It used to be considered a fatal disease.

**Lo'omatua**— An abscess in the armpit. Literally, "old woman." Pratt noted instead the name "*tama'ita'i*," which means young woman. See **ma'i sua**.

—M—

**Ma'alili**— Shivering. Literally, "cold."

**Magemage**— See **manemane**.

**Mageso**— A rash or itch, perhaps often scabies.

**Mageso le totoga sā**— Itchy genitals in women; yeast infection.

**Maʻi**— The general word for illness. Compare **gasegase.**

**Maʻi afi**— Venereal disease, gonorrhea. Literally, "fire sickness."

**Maʻi aitu**— Mental illness, usually temporary in nature and believed to be a result of supernatural causes. "Possession."

**Maʻi ate**— General term for any ailment of the liver.

**Maʻi fasia**— Another name for **maʻi aitu.**

**Maʻi gau**— A serious or recurring illness, sometimes described as flu-like, possibly one that was not successfully treated the first time. Relapse fever.

**Maʻi manava**— General term for any stomach problem.

**Maʻi masina**— Menstruation, literally "monthly sickness." See **punatoto** and **piliki.**

**Maʻi mata**— General term for eye ailment, often a red, swollen eye (conjunctivitis).

**Maʻi oso**— Possibly convulsions.

**Maʻi ʻo tane**— A polite word for **fifi paū**, hernia.

**Maʻi sua**— General term for boils, especially on the limbs. See also **ʻoloā, silaʻilagi, silaʻilalo,** and **loʻomatua.**

**Maʻi sua ua luga**— A throbbing, unincised boil.

**Maʻi suka**— Diabetes, literally, "sugar sickness."

**Maʻi tafafao**— Kind of **maʻi aitu** that is contracted by being too irreverant or playful. *Tafafao* (singular, *tafao*) means to fool or play around.

**Māmāpala**— Tuberculosis. Literally, "rotten lungs." Also called **fatafata vaivai** by some healers.

**Manava**— Stomach. Also a shortened form of **manava tīgā.**

**Manava fefete**— Gassy or swollen stomach, or abdominal distress due to indigestion. The Macphersons noted it to be a flatulent condition caused by overeating.

**Manava mamau**— Constipation. The Macphersons described it as a type of constipation with associated displacement of the *toʻala*, but it is probably more often just considered constipation.

**Manava oso**— Acute abdominal distress. It was defined by the Macphersons as "sudden inexplicable, and occasionally fatal, stresses that are marked by rapid onset of severe pain." *Oso* means to jump.

**Manava tafe**— Another name for **manava tatā.**

**Manava tatā**— Diarrhea. See also **tulatula, manava tafe,** and **muli sī.**

**Manava tīgā**— Stomachache.

**Manava tutui**— Acute abdominal pain.

**Manemane**— Skin condition on the soles of the feet. Pratt defined it as "a disease that eats away the skin of the palms of the hands and the soles of the feet." Also spelled **magemage.**

**Manuʻa**— A wound, often used interchangeably with **lavea.**

**Manuʻa ʻona**— Infected wound.

**Mata ʻavea**— Blurry vision, thought to be a type of **maʻi aitu** caused by the person spending too much time outside in the evening when the *aitu* are most likely to be out.

**Matafā**— Sty, a boil near the eye. Called by the same name in Tonga.

**Mata māsae**— Eye injury or laceration, literally "torn eye," involving pain and the discharge of fluid.

**Mata o le i'a**— Protruding flesh, usually from the ends of the toes and fingertips, caused by an infected puncture wound.

**Mata pa'ia**— Eye injury, caused by a foreign object poking, becoming lodged in (like a particle of dirt), or brushing against the eye.

**Mata puaoa**— Blurry vision.

**Matate**— Loss of appetite for food or drink, caused by a throat or mouth infection.

**Matolo**— A large blister on the scalp, possibly an infected one causing throbbing and pain.

**Misela**— Measles, a transliteration of the name. This is not usually treated by Samoan healers.

**Moālili**— A white membrane that forms over the eye, possibly the same as **tū**, pterygium. The Macphersons defined it as corneal scars on the eye itself.

**Moa tigā**— Abdominal pain. *Moa* is the solar plexus.

**Mo'omo'o**— A one-sided migraine headache. Milner defined it as a longing for something, and Pratt simply as a disease. The Macphersons noted that it is believed to have a supernatural origin.

**Mū**— A burn. Also, a type of baby's rash, diaper or nappy rash.

**Muli si**— Impolite word for **manava tatā.**

**Mūmū**— A group of ailments characterized by some degree of skin inflammation (cellulitis) and raised temperature, but which vary considerably beyond that.

**Mūmū a'ano**— Inflammation with open sores, possibly from diabetes.

**Mūmū afi**— Possibly inflammation manifested by an inflamed anal area. McCuddin described it as an illness of adults or children manifested by pustules that spread when broken; "cellulitis with lymphagitis and fever."

**Mūmū asuafi**— Inflammation of the skin accompanied by small white blisters, often of children. The blisters are red one day and white the next. Possibly scabies or impetigo, or both.

**Mūmū lele**— A serious and sometimes fatal type of cellulitis and fever of children and adults that rapidly spreads from a limb. McCuddin compared this to fatal septicemia. The Macphersons noted the appearance of red spots on the body, and Cox said it is characterized by high fever and paralysis.

**Mūmū lili**— An ailment of infants characterized by fever, dizziness, and seizures.

**Mūmū mageso**— A type of inflammation characterized by itchy skin rashes.

**Mūmū melo**— An inflammation of infants characterized by rough red skin, especially around the anus. Milner defined *melo* as "being about to cry."

**Mūmū oso**— Acute fever and inflammation, appearing unexpectedly (literally, "jumping up").

**Mūmū pata**— A skin infection (dermatitis) characterized by reddish blotches on the skin. Also called **pata.**

**Mūmū sāua**— Chills and headache of mysterious origin, thought to be caused by the actions of spirits when the patient has stayed out too late at night.

**Mūmū ta'ai**— Type of inflammation with fever, characterized by difficult or shallow breathing, according to the Macphersons. Possibly an upper respiratory tract infection. Compare **fiva ta'ai.**

**Mūmū tatau**— An inflammatory skin ailment, mostly of children, characterized by the skin turning black, starting from the buttocks. The Macphersons noted that the discoloration occurs on the soles of the feet and palms of the hands.

**Mūmū tuaʻula**— An inflammatory ailment of children and babies manifested by red skin blotches, fever (feeling hot inside), sleeplessness, lack of sweating, and often a headache. McCuddin described it as "cellulitis with septicemia."

**Mūmū tuaʻula uli**— Ailment of children and adults manifested by dizziness, cold sweat, sore eyes, and numbness in the legs. The Macphersons noted that the discoloration is confined to the soles of the feet.

—N—

**Nifoa**— Teething of babies.
**Nifo tīgā**— Toothache.
**Nīmonia**— Pneumonia, but noted in Milner as "*fiva limōnia.*" See also **limonia**.
**Nunu**— Arthritis of the joints.

—O—

**Ogoogo**— Eye irritation or sore eyes, sometimes spelled **ogo**. Pratt defined **ogo** as a disease of children's eyes; Krämer noted that Pratt defined it as sunburn.

**ʻOloā**— A chronic abscess, possibly from diabetes or an improperly treated boil. It is believed to be caused by the bite of a spirit known as Nifoloa, who protects people from Falelima, Savaiʻi. The hardened core of the boil or wound is called the *nifo* (tooth) or *atilo*, which upon emerging is burned to prevent anyone else from being affected. Some healers note two or three types. See **maʻi sua**.

**ʻOloā sami**— A type of infected wound, not necessarily coming from the sea (*sami*).

**ʻOna**— Tetanus, typically contracted from a puncture wound. Called *kona hamu* in Tonga.

**ʻŌnā**— Sickness of a baby being nursed by a mother who has become pregnant again.

**ʻŌnā**— Food poisoning, from eating tainted fish or other food.

**Osofā punimoa**— A stomach ailment, or possibly intestinal blockage or acute indigestion, described by the Macphersons as preventing food from entering the stomach. Cox noted that this is believed to be caused by the *toʻala* moving up and blocking the entrance to the stomach. It may sometimes be shortened to **osofā**. Literally, "blocked jumping of the solar plexus."

—P—

**Pala**— General term for infections, but more specifically applying to those in the mouth (stomatitis). Called by the same name in Tonga.

**Pala fefie**— A type of mouth infection of infants manifested by swollen, bleeding gums; gingivitis and stomatitis. Called by the same name in Tonga.

**Pala gaʻau**— Stomach or intestinal ulcers, or stomach cancer. Literally, "rotten intestines." Called *pala ngakau* in Tonga.

**Pala gutu**— Stomatitis, sometimes shortened to **pala**, or reversed as **gutu pala**. Called by the same name in Tonga (*pala ngutu*).

**Pala mūmū**— Inflammation or infection of the nasal mucous membrane; rhinitis.

**Palapala**— Menstrual or afterbirth blood. Literally, "dirt."

**Papala**— General term for skin sores or ulcers, typically covering the body. A single sore is a **poʻu**.

**Pata**— A kind of rash or itchiness. Also called **mūmū pata**. Compare **supa vai**.

**Pī**— A wasp or bee, and their sting.

**Pī faʻalau sosoʻo**— Frequent urination.

**Piliki**— Dysmenorrhea, difficult or painful menstruation, but more commonly called **punatoto**. This is a transliteration of the English word "bleed." See also **maʻi masina**.

**Poʻu**— Skin sores. **Poʻua** means covered with sores. See also **papala**.

**Poʻu matatele**— A large sore. Literally, "big-eyed sore."

**Poʻu sā**— Sores on the skin, impetigo. McCuddin noted that it usually starts on a leg and spreads, and that there is no Western treatment for this. It leaves permanent white blotches on the skin.

**Puaʻi**— Vomiting.

**Puaoa**— Poor or blurred vision.

**Puga**— Swollen and infected lymph node in the groin.

**Punatoto**— Dysmenorrhea, excessive, painful, or prolonged menstrual flow. See also **piliki**, **maʻi masina**.

—S—

**Sagatoto**— Dysentery, diarrhea with blood in the feces. Literally, "persistent bleeding." In Tonga, *hana* is the word for diarrhea.

**Saga vai**— Incessant urination. *Saga* means persistent and *vai* means water.

**Sāua**— A sickness that is believed to be caused, or is prevented from healing, by supernatural means (i.e., by an *aitu*).

**Sela**— Difficulty in breathing, asthma, or bronchitis, characterized by shortness of breath. See also **gaʻe**. Called *hela* in Tonga.

**Silaʻilagi**— A boil or carbuncle occurring on the upper part of the body, most frequently on the abdomen, back, or back of the neck. Called *hilaʻakilangi* in Tonga, where it is defined as a boil on the back. See **maʻi sua**.

**Silaʻilalo**— A boil around the anus, buttocks, and genitals. Pratt defined it as piles. See **maʻi sua**. Called *hilaʻakilalo* in Tonga.

**Sulufa**— Herniated disc in the back.

**Supa vai**— Probably swollen allergenic skin rashes, possibly the same as **pata**.

—T—

**Tafe fāua**— Excessive salivation.

**Tāgulugulu**— Excessive snoring.

**Tale**— Cough. Called by the same name in Tonga.

**Tane**— Skin fungus, *Tinea versicolor*, characterized by rough white blotches on the skin. Called by the same name in Tonga.

**Tīgā**— General term for pain.

**Tīgā tutui**— Serious or throbbing pain.

**To'ala (or to'oala)**— Abdominal pain possibly resulting from intestinal obstruction or a displaced organ. Samoan healers believe it is caused by the displacement of an intangible organ, the *to'ala* or *to'oala*, that is normally located under the solar plexus. Most healers believe it occurs in both men and women, but is more characteristic of women and is concerned with reproduction. Called *toka'ala* in Tonga and Tokelau.

**Tona**— Yaws, a non-venereal disease related to syphilis that has now been eradicated from Samoa. Called by the same name in Tonga.

**To'omaunu**— Hiccups.

**To'oto'oma'a**— A pain usually found in the palm of the hand or sole of the foot, possibly from a puncture wound, and sometimes attributed to walking barefooted.

**Toto maualuga**— High blood pressure, hypertension.

**Tū**— Pterygium, a growth of tissue across the cornea of the eye. Possibly the same as **moālili**.

**Tua tīgā**— Backache.

**Tuia**— A puncture wound from the sting of a poisonous fish such as *gofu* (stonefish).

**Tulatula**— Diarrhea with stools having white or yellow blood deposits in them. See also **manava tatā** and **muli sī**. Some healers believe that it is caused by eating too many sweets.

**Tulilefu**— Acute arthritis of the knee, with the patient being unable to straighten out the leg.

**Tulitā**— A group of several ailments that affect the urinary tract, commonly bladder infection (cystitis) associated with frequent urination.

**Tulitā fa'afaiavāina**— Type of **tulitā** characterized by impeded urination, believed to be caused by the actions of the ghost (*aitu*) of a recently deceased spouse.

**Tulitā fasia**— Urinary tract infection manifested by painful urination. McCuddin and the Macphersons noted that it is thought to be caused by an *aitu*.

**Tulitā filēmū**— A painless kind of diarrhea that causes weight loss. Cox described it as incontinence.

**Tulitā mamau**— Difficult urination, dysuria.

**Tulitā sāua**— Abdominal pain, or perhaps pain in the urinary tract, believed to be caused by the actions of *aitu* as punishment for some activity, such as defecating near a graveyard sometime in the past. Cox noted it is characterized by bloody stools and partial paralysis.

**Tulitā tīgā**— A painful type of **tulitā**. Defined by the Macphersons as "painful urination."

**Tupa**— Elephantiasis, permanent swelling of a limb caused by filariasis, an ailment now virtually eliminated from Samoa. **Vaetupa** means elephantiasis of a leg.

—U—

**'Ula**— An allergenic skin rash usually occurring on the neck.

**Ulu tīgā**— Headache.

**Una'i'a**— A cataract.

**Uno'o**— A bruise. **Uno'oa** means to be bruised.

**'Utu**— A fungal skin infection something like ringworm, occurring mostly on the palms of the hands or on the feet.

—V—

**Vae gau**— Broken leg.

**Vaeluaina**— Type of ailment in which the body seems to be divided in two, with some parts warm and other parts cold.

**Vae tupa**— See **tupa**.

**Vevela**— Fever. Literally, "hot." See **fiva**.

# LIST OF FIGURES

# INDEX TO SCIENTIFIC NAMES

*Synonyms are in italics.*

# INDEX TO SAMOAN NAMES

# ADDENDUM

Two other plant species have come to my attention that may be used medicinally to some extent, but which didn't turn up during the regular survey. The first, a small tree of the pea family Fabaceae, *Bauhinia monandra* Kurz (**vae povi**, orchid tree), has showy pink to purple flowers and deeply notched leaves (like the footprint of a cow, "*vae povi*"). It is reported to be used as a treatment for sunburn, on Tutuila at least.

The second species, *Catharanthus roseus* (L.) G. Don (Madagascar periwinkle) of the dogbane family Apocynaceae, can be distinguished by its showy pink or white flowers and milky sap. Four different Samoan names were given to it—**fetū**, **mata ole lā**, **pua sosolo**, and **falaoa mata violē**—by four different informants. All these names are questionable. This periwinkle was also given a variety of names in the Cook Islands (Whistler 1985). Two healers contacted after the regular survey both noted this plant being used for treating high blood pressure, in very similar remedies.

Additionally, a European physician in Samoa noted that the ailment called *nifoloa* is actually a bone infection (osteomyelitis) that causes pieces of bone to come to the surface (the *atilo* of Samoan medicine).

A. W.
March 1996

# NOTES

# NOTES

# NOTES

"We don't inherit the earth;
we borrow it from our children."

O le Siosiomaga Society was originally established by the Swedish Nature Society in 1990, partially to manage its conservation projects in Western Samoa. We are Western Samoa's non-governmental organisation for the conservation of our natural heritage—so that future generations can experience and enjoy it. Our stated purposes are to provide information to the public, to organize meetings and panel discussions, and to produce videos and publications on enviromental issues such as (1) rain forest protection; (2) watershed management; (3) coastal protection; (4) mangrove protection; (5) protection of endangered species; (6) reef protection; (7) waste management; and (8) sustainable development.

The Society is managed by an elected board consisting of a President and six Board Members. The Director and Office Manager carry out the day-to-day running of the office, which is located in Apia. For further information on publications or other matters, or if you would like to become a member, write

O le Siosiomaga Society Inc.
P. O. Box 5774
Matautu-uta
Western Samoa
PH.& FAX: (685) 21993